Vocabulary WORKS

Level D

Joy Tweedt   Craig Tweed & Dr. Alvin Granowsky

Copyright © 1995 by Modern Curriculum Press, Inc.

An imprint of Paramount Supplemental Education
299 Jefferson Road
Parsippany, New Jersey 07054

ISBN 0-8136-1711-1

   6 7 8 9 10   98

TABLE OF CONTENTS

SLAP SHOT SENDS PUCK SOARING
OFFICIAL BLOWS THE WHISTLE

Look out! The player is bound for the **goal** at lightning speed! **Defensive** teammates seem **fearless** as they **streak** down the ice looking to **check** an opponent into the boards. And they do! With a slap shot the puck soars past the goalie! It's in! A whistle signals more bad news for the opponents! The call? A **penalty** of two minutes in the box for tripping!

Ice hockey is a fast and **exciting** sport first played in Canada in the 1850s. Protected by helmets, plenty of padding, and sometimes masks, hockey players must be able to **skate** forwards and **backwards** at top speed. They must make sharp turns and stop on a dime.

Hockey players must also be expert stick handlers. A powerful slap or wrist shot can send the small rubber disc racing like a **missile** at speeds up to 100 miles per hour.

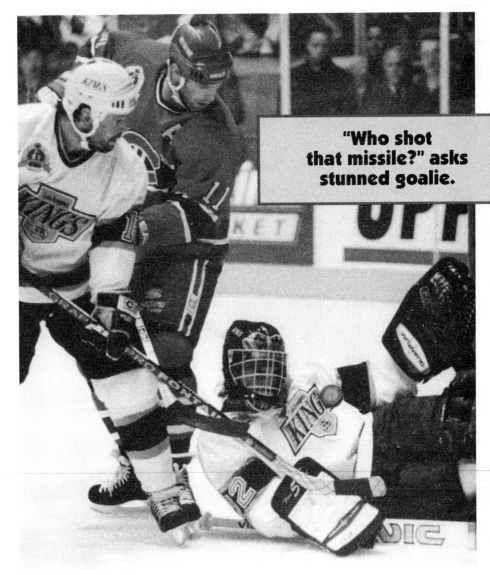

"Who shot that missile?" asks stunned goalie.

Ice hockey has become so popular among men and women that even young children are gearing up to chase the puck. And no wonder! It is a sport that combines speed, skill, and lots of fun.

DETAIL CHECK

Hockey was first played in _____ .

Check the best answer.

○ Canada

○ Russia

○ the United States

○ the 1950s

ALPHABET KEEPS WORDS IN ORDER

Write the New Words in alphabetical order on the lines.

NEW WORDS

goal

defensive

fearless

streak

check

penalty

missile

exciting

skate

backwards

1. _____   6. _____

2. _____   7. _____

3. _____   8. _____

4. _____   9. _____

5. _____   10. _____

WORDS AND MEANINGS TEAM UP FOR EXCITING MATCH

☞ **Context clues** are words in a sentence or phrase that help you understand the meaning of a word. Look for context clues to help you match each New Word with its meaning.

Write the correct letter on each line.

____ 1. goal

____ 2. defensive

____ 3. fearless

____ 4. streak

____ 5. check

____ 6. penalty

____ 7. missile

____ 8. exciting

____ 9. skate

____ 10. backwards

a. in the direction opposite from which one is facing

b. in hockey, the area into which the puck must be hit to score a point; the act of getting the puck in this area

c. to move at a very fast speed

d. with the intent of preventing attack or protecting something

e. brave; unafraid

f. stimulating or thrilling

g. an object made to be thrown or shot at a target

h. in hockey, to block an opponent

i. punishment for breaking a rule or law

j. to slide along the ice on metal blades

4

COMPLETED SENTENCES SCORE BIG

Use New Words to finish the sentences.

1. Soccer is a very _____ game.

2. Players _____ forwards and backwards on the field.

3. Tyrone scored a _____ with only three seconds left in the game.

4. Everyone was happy that there was no _____ on the play.

5. _____ players keep the other team from scoring.

6. They have to be _____ while they play.

7. The player went so fast she looked like a _____ .

8. Sarah had to _____ the other player to stop her from scoring.

9. Chris learned how to _____ this year.

10. He found that skating _____ was very hard.

MULTIPLE MEANINGS MAKE WORDS MEAN MORE

 Many words have **multiple meanings**. Context clues can tell you which meaning fits.

right can mean a direction or to be correct

Read the meanings given for the words below.

goal
a. an area where points are scored
b. an end to be achieved

check
a. to block an opponent
b. to make sure about something

skate
a. to slide on ice on metal blades
b. a type of sea creature

streak
a. to move quickly
b. a smear of dirt or grease

Now use context clues to find the right meaning for the underlined words in the sentences. Write either a or b on each line.

____ 1. The hockey player scored another goal.

____ 2. My goal is to become a lawyer.

____ 3. Please check to make sure the door is locked.

____ 4. It takes strength to check an opponent.

____ 5. We saw a skate when we went swimming in the ocean.

____ 6. I like to skate on the pond.

____ 7. The runners streak by at a fast pace.

____ 8. There's a streak on that window.

5

THE TRUTH ABOUT CATEGORIES

👉 A **category** is a group to which similiar things belong.

Cars, **trucks**, and **buses** go together under the category <u>land vehicles</u>.

Read each category and circle the three words or phrases that belong.

1. people who <u>skate</u>
   - hockey players
   - figure skaters
   - doctors
   - speed skaters

2. kinds of <u>goals</u>
   - touchdown
   - puck
   - home run
   - basket

3. things to <u>check</u>
   - the lights
   - the door
   - the weather
   - defensive

4. <u>fast</u> things
   - car
   - audience
   - skater
   - jet

5. exciting sports
   - basketball
   - football
   - practice
   - hockey

Don't get penalized. Take the test!

6

CHECK AND SCORE!
READ:

- "Hockey's Masked Men." (*Boys' Life*, March, 1993)
- "Cutting Edge." (*National Geographic World*, February, 1993)
- "Wayne Gretsky" in *Great Athletes: The Twentieth Century.* (Salem Press, 1992)

WATCH:

- *The Mighty Ducks.* (a Walt Disney video)

SPORT SPOT!

A hockey goalie's equipment can weigh up to 20 pounds.

HOCKEY TERMS EXPLAINED

❋ A **slap shot** is a hard shot made with a full swing of the hockey stick. A slap shot sometimes makes the puck leave the ice.

❋ A **wrist shot** is an easier shot made with the wrist.

❋ To **check** an opponent **into the boards** is to bump a skater from the other team so that he or she skates into the wall at the edge of the rink.

❋ The **penalty box** is a place outside the rink where a player must go if he or she breaks one of the rules.

UP CLOSE AND PERSONAL
PROFILE OF A HOCKEY PLAYER

📝 Look at the picture. Write a story about this hockey player.

 Thinking about these questions will help guide your writing:

- How did the hockey player feel the first time he scored a goal?
- How did he become a professional hockey player?
- Why does he like playing hockey?

Use at least four New Words in your story.

TEST-TAKING SECRETS REVEALED

Mark your answers with a sharpened, no. 2 pencil. Have several handy in case one breaks.

---

*Read each group of words. Select the word or words that mean the **same** as the underlined word. Fill in the circle for the answer at the bottom of the page.*

1   <u>skate</u> on the ice

   A   move on special shoes
   B   fall
   C   slip
   D   slide on skis

2   <u>streak</u> across the field

   A   trot
   B   speed
   C   walk
   D   see

3   <u>check</u> the player

   A   help
   B   mark
   C   hold back
   D   hit hard

4   hit the <u>goal</u>

   A   scoring net
   B   player
   C   opponent
   D   wooden stick

5   shot a <u>missile</u>

   A   gun
   B   racing train
   C   thrown object
   D   firecracker

6   given a <u>penalty</u>

   A   player
   B   score
   C   team
   D   punishment

7   a <u>defensive</u> move

   A   protecting
   B   scoring
   C   skating
   D   tripping

8   a <u>fearless</u> player

   A   fast
   B   skillful
   C   brave
   D   afraid

---

*Read each group of words. Select the word or words that mean the **opposite** of the underlined word. Fill in the circle for the answer at the bottom of the page.*

9   a <u>fearless</u> soldier

   A   courageous   **C**   cowardly
   B   brave   **D**   smart

10   moving <u>backwards</u>

   A   sideways   **C**   toward the back
   B   forward   **D**   toward the side

11   an <u>exciting</u> event

   A   boring   **C**   sports
   B   usual   **D**   thrilling

12   <u>defensive</u> players

   A   blockers   **C**   protecting
   B   offensive   **D**   skilled

ANSWERS						
1	Ⓐ Ⓑ Ⓒ Ⓓ	4	Ⓐ Ⓑ Ⓒ Ⓓ	7	Ⓐ Ⓑ Ⓒ Ⓓ	10 Ⓐ Ⓑ Ⓒ Ⓓ
2	Ⓐ Ⓑ Ⓒ Ⓓ	5	Ⓐ Ⓑ Ⓒ Ⓓ	8	Ⓐ Ⓑ Ⓒ Ⓓ	11 Ⓐ Ⓑ Ⓒ Ⓓ
3	Ⓐ Ⓑ Ⓒ Ⓓ	6	Ⓐ Ⓑ Ⓒ Ⓓ	9	Ⓐ Ⓑ Ⓒ Ⓓ	12 Ⓐ Ⓑ Ⓒ Ⓓ

INSECTS BEWARE!
THIS PLANT BITES

"I'll take two flies and an ant... to go!"

The fly wanted a place to rest. That leaf looked **cozy**. The fly landed. Snap! In half a second the plant's leaf snapped shut. The Venus' flytrap had another meal to eat.

The Venus' flytrap is one of very **few** carnivorous, or meat-eating, plants. The leaves look like two **ovals** joined on one side with **spines** around the edge. Each oval has three short hairs. When an insect lands on the leaf, these hairs **signal** the leaf to close. The leaf closes so quickly that the insect does not have time to escape. The spines form a **prison** around the insect.

The Venus' flytrap **digests** the insect for food. Therefore, it can live in **soil** where many other plants cannot grow.

Once an insect is trapped and digested, the leaves unfold to trap another. After a leaf has digested a few insects, the leaf dies, and a new one takes its place.

Since this plant is so unusual, the Venus' flytrap is a **popular** houseplant. Children and grown-ups enjoy feeding a bit of **raw** meat to the plant. Would you?

DETAIL DIGEST

Which statement about the Venus' flytrap is <u>not</u> true?
Check the best answer.

❑ The Venus' flytrap is a popular houseplant.
❑ The Venus' flytrap is a meat-eating plant.
❑ Insects like to eat the Venus' flytrap.
❑ Children enjoy feeding the Venus' flytrap.

WORDS NEED ALPHABET TO STAY IN ORDER

Write the New Words in alphabetical order.

NEW WORDS

few
spines
digests
ovals
popular
cozy
prison
signal
soil
raw

1. _____

2. _____

3. _____

4. _____

5. _____

6. _____

7. _____

8. _____

9. _____

10. _____

MATCHING WORDS WITH MEANINGS—IT'S A SNAP

Use context clues or the glossary to match each New Word below with its meaning.

Write the correct letter on each line.

____ 1. spines

____ 2. ovals

____ 3. soil

____ 4. raw

____ 5. few

____ 6. cozy

____ 7. prison

____ 8. popular

____ 9. digests

____ 10. signal

a. warm and comfortable; snug

b. the top layer of earth in which plants grow; ground

c. a place where people or things are shut up

d. to give a sign that warns, directs, or informs

e. thin, sharp, or stiff parts that stick out on certain plants and animals

f. liked by many people

g. changes or breaks down food into a form that can be used by an organism

h. things shaped like an egg or like an ellipse

i. not many; a small number of

j. not cooked

MISSING WORDS CAPTURED

Finish these sentences. Write a New Word on each line.

NEW WORDS

cozy

ovals

raw

signal

soil

few

spines

prison

digests

popular

1. Mr. Jackson likes to sit in his

   _____ living room.

2. He rests while his dinner _____ .

3. Carrots are a root that grows

   in the _____ .

4. They can be eaten _____ or cooked.

5. The starter's job was to _____ the race to begin.

6. The runners finished the race in just a _____

   minutes.

7. These cactuses are shaped like _____ .

8. They have _____ instead of leaves.

9. The criminal was sentenced to 25 years in _____ .

10. Because of his crime, he was not _____ with many people.

SPEAKING OF SYNONYMS...

Synonyms are words with nearly the same meaning.

dish and **plate**   **sofa** and **couch**

Write the New Words that are synonyms for the words below.

1. uncooked _____

2. well-liked _____

3. several _____

4. spikes _____

5. jail _____

6. comfortable _____

7. egg-shapes _____

8. dirt _____

BETWEEN ONE THING AND ANOTHER—ANALOGIES

 Analogies show the relationship between things.

meow is to **cat** as **bark** is to **dog**

hand is to **glove** as **foot** is to **shoe**

Use a New Word to finish each sentence.

1. <u>plant</u> is to _____ as <u>fish</u> is to <u>water</u>

2. <u>rectangles</u> is to <u>squares</u> as _____ is to <u>circles</u>

3. <u>lost</u> is to <u>found</u> as _____ is to <u>cooked</u>

4. <u>thorns</u> is to <u>rose</u> as _____ is to <u>cactus</u>

5. <u>cage</u> is to <u>bird</u> as _____ is to <u>thief</u>

MYSTERY PLANT DISCOVERED

Imagine that you just discovered this plant pictured below. Write a paragraph describing it.

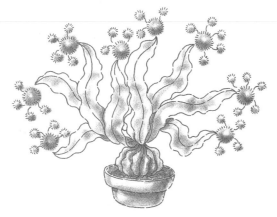

These questions will help guide your writing:

- How tall is the plant?
- What do its leaves and flowers look like?
- What type of climate does it grow in?

Use at least four New Words in your paragraph.

Don't get captured, take the test!

SCORE HIGHER ON TESTS

When looking for a word that means the opposite of a given word, don't be fooled by a choice that means the same.

Read each group of words. Select the word or words that mean the <u>opposite</u> of the underlined word. Fill in the circle for the answer at the bottom of the page.

1   a <u>raw</u> potato

   A   uncooked   **C**   small
   B   baked   **D**   sweet

2   a <u>few</u> days

   A   sunny   **C**   great number
   B   small number **D**   two

3   a <u>cozy</u> room

   A   large   **C**   snug
   B   hot   **D**   uncomfortable

4   a <u>popular</u> show

   A   disliked   **C**   long
   B   well-liked **D**   quiet

Read each set of sentences. Select the word or words that best complete the second sentence in each set. Fill in the circle for the answer at the bottom of the page.

5   The traffic lights <u>signal</u> the cars to stop.
   <u>Signal</u> means—

   A   warn or direct
   B   drive or fly
   C   finish
   D   begin

6   Those picture frames are shaped like <u>ovals</u>.
   <u>Ovals</u> means—

   A   spikes
   B   egg-shapes
   C   squares
   D   circles

7   The stomach <u>digests</u> food to be used in the body.
   <u>Digests</u> means—

   A   delivers
   B   cooks
   C   gives
   D   changes

8   A <u>prison</u> is being built near our home.
   <u>Prison</u> means—

   A   school
   B   building
   C   jail
   D   library

9   I pricked my finger on the <u>spines</u> of the cactus.
   <u>Spines</u> means—

   A   water
   B   roots
   C   fruit
   D   spikes

10   He turned the <u>soil</u> to get it ready for planting.
   <u>Soil</u> means—

   A   dirt
   B   plants
   C   shovel
   D   garden

11   I eat a <u>raw</u> apple every day.
   <u>Raw</u> means—

   A   red
   B   green
   C   uncooked
   D   sliced

12   There are a <u>few</u> people still working on the project.
   <u>Few</u> means—

   A   busy
   B   several
   C   crowd
   D   dozen

ANSWERS

1	Ⓐ Ⓑ Ⓒ Ⓓ	4	Ⓐ Ⓑ Ⓒ Ⓓ	7	Ⓐ Ⓑ Ⓒ Ⓓ	10	Ⓐ Ⓑ Ⓒ Ⓓ
2	Ⓐ Ⓑ Ⓒ Ⓓ	5	Ⓐ Ⓑ Ⓒ Ⓓ	8	Ⓐ Ⓑ Ⓒ Ⓓ	11	Ⓐ Ⓑ Ⓒ Ⓓ
3	Ⓐ Ⓑ Ⓒ Ⓓ	6	Ⓐ Ⓑ Ⓒ Ⓓ	9	Ⓐ Ⓑ Ⓒ Ⓓ	12	Ⓐ Ⓑ Ⓒ Ⓓ

NO BONES ABOUT IT

SPINELESS OCTOPUS SEEKS SOLITUDE

The class laughed. Mrs. Johnson **silenced** the children.

"Cindy's right. An octopus **gathers** seaweed and rocks to make its nest. It hides there until its babies go out on their own. When an octopus is afraid, it sprays out a black **liquid**. It swims away while its **enemy** can't see in the cloudy water."

"Maybe it's **shy** because it looks so strange!" said Scott.

"The octopus does look strange," agreed Mrs. Johnson. "It has no **skeleton** or bones. Some grow larger than a person, but most are no bigger than a human hand. Its shiny eyes stick out of its balloon-shaped body. Its eight **tentacles** have rows of round **muscles** that fasten tightly to shellfish. The tentacles do not squeeze. They pull the shellfish to the octopus's **dangerous** jaws. **Death** comes with a poisonous bite. While shellfish are food for the octopus, the octopus is often food for other animals. That's why it's so shy!"

"Did you know that an octopus makes a nest?" *exclaimed Cindy.*

WHAT WAS THAT NUMBER AGAIN?

How many tentacles does an octopus have?

Check the best answer.

◯ four   ◯ six   ◯ eight   ◯ ten

THE AMAZING ALPHABET

Write the New Words in alphabetical order.

1. _____

2. _____

3. _____

4. _____

5. _____

6. _____

7. _____

8. _____

9. _____

10. _____

NEW WORDS

dangerous

shy

death

muscles

gathers

tentacles

enemy

skeleton

liquid

silenced

REMEDY FOR MEANINGLESS WORDS

Use context clues or the glossary to match each New Word with its meaning.

Write the letter of the meaning on the line next to the word.

____ 1. enemy

____ 2. muscles

____ 3. liquid

____ 4. dangerous

____ 5. silenced

____ 6. gathers

____ 7. shy

____ 8. tentacles

____ 9. death

____ 10. skeleton

a. full of danger; likely to cause injury or pain

b. brings or comes together in one place

c. long, slender parts of some animals used for feeling, gripping, or moving

d. a person, animal, or group that hates or fights against another

e. easily frightened; timid

f. the framework of bones of an animal's body

g. a substance that flows easily; matter that is neither a solid nor a gas

h. made silent; made still

i. the tissues in an animal's body that can be stretched or tightened to move the parts of the body

j. the act or fact of dying; ending of life

INCOMPLETE SENTENCES CLOUD THE ISSUE

Finish these sentences. Write a New Word on each line.

1. Mrs. Johnson _____ the class when it became noisy.

2. She taught her students the following facts about

   the _____ octopus.

3. The octopus _____ rocks and seaweed to build its nest.

4. The snake-like arms of the octopus are called _____ .

5. The tentacles can be bent in any direction since the octopus has no

   _____ .

6. Round _____ can fasten tightly to shellfish.

7. The octopus sprays a black _____ called ink when

   an enemy comes near.

8. Sharks, whales, and humans are all the _____ of

   the octopus.

9. It is _____ to handle an octopus because of its bite.

10. The bite may not cause _____ , but it does hurt.

ANTONYMS MAKE A DIFFERENCE IN MEANING

☞ **Antonyms** are words that have opposite meanings.

quick and **slow**   **new** and **old**

Use the New Words to find an antonym for each puzzle. Then write the antonyms in the boxes.

1. S O L I D

2. L I F E

3. S A F E

4. F R I E N D L Y

5. F R I E N D

15

THIS SPINELESS CREATURE HAS QUITE A STING

 Look at the picture. Write five sentences comparing this jellyfish to the octopus.

These questions will help guide your writing:

• Do you think the jellyfish has a skeleton?

• How do you think it eats?

• Does it look friendly?

Use at least four New Words in your sentences.

INK BLURS SIGHT AND SMELL

An octopus's ink cloud does more than just make it difficult to see. The inky substance can also paralyze an attacker's sense of smell.

READ MORE ABOUT IT

• *Octopus* by Carol Carrick. (Clarion, 1978)

• *Herman the Helper* by Robert Kraus. (Simon & Schuster, 1987)

• *An Octopus Is Amazing* by Patricia Lauber. (Crowell, 1990)

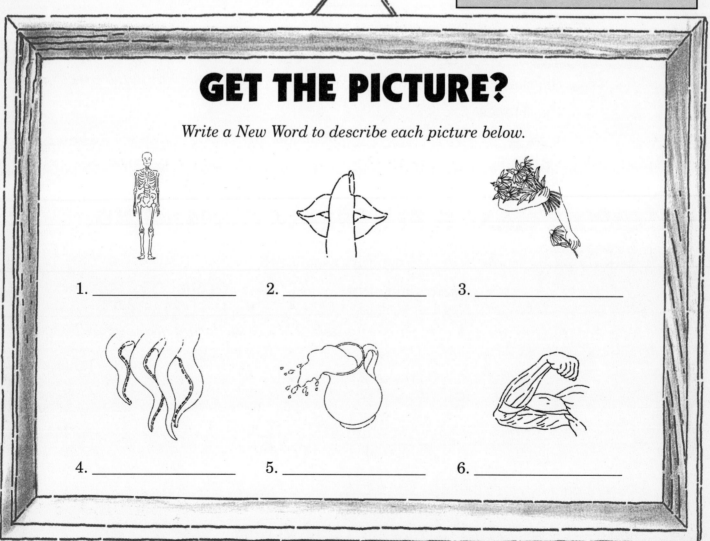

GET THE PICTURE?

Write a New Word to describe each picture below.

1. _____

2. _____

3. _____

4. _____

5. _____

6. _____

Ink in the answers on the test!

TEST-DAY TIPS TOLD

On test day, bring your own eraser and make sure it erases cleanly.

Complete each definition with the best word or words. Fill in the circle for the answer at the bottom of the page.

1 The long arms on an octopus are called . . . .

   A skeleton
   B muscles
   C tentacles
   D dangerous

2 To be quieted is to be . . . .

   A silenced
   B angered
   C pushed
   D carried

3 A bashful person is . . . .

   A bold
   B silenced
   C dangerous
   D shy

4 A foe is a person who is . . . .

   A a friend
   B an enemy
   C a partner
   D an actor

5 Matter that is neither gas nor solid is . . . .

   A skeleton
   B shy
   C dangerous
   D liquid

6 Someone who brings things together . . . .

   A scatters
   B gathers
   C muscles
   D makes

Read each sentence. Select the word or words that best complete each one. Fill in the circle for the answer at the bottom of the page.

7 The _____ in his arms ached from overuse.

   A legs
   B tentacles
   C muscles
   D knees

8 The doctor used a _____ to point out the bones in the body.

   A skeleton
   B liquid
   C death
   D solid

9 Your habit of walking near the side of the road is _____.

   A silenced
   B dangerous
   C shy
   D death

10 That poison can cause _____.

   A tentacles
   B broken bones
   C loss of money
   D death

11 The _____ boy was not sure of himself.

   A dangerous
   B bold
   C shy
   D unjust

12 I poured the _____ into the bottle.

   A muscles
   B skeleton
   C tentacles
   D liquid

ANSWERS

1	Ⓐ Ⓑ Ⓒ Ⓓ	4	Ⓐ Ⓑ Ⓒ Ⓓ	7	Ⓐ Ⓑ Ⓒ Ⓓ	10	Ⓐ Ⓑ Ⓒ Ⓓ
2	Ⓐ Ⓑ Ⓒ Ⓓ	5	Ⓐ Ⓑ Ⓒ Ⓓ	8	Ⓐ Ⓑ Ⓒ Ⓓ	11	Ⓐ Ⓑ Ⓒ Ⓓ
3	Ⓐ Ⓑ Ⓒ Ⓓ	6	Ⓐ Ⓑ Ⓒ Ⓓ	9	Ⓐ Ⓑ Ⓒ Ⓓ	12	Ⓐ Ⓑ Ⓒ Ⓓ

THE MORE NAMES CHANGE— THE MORE THEY STAY THE SAME

Names are a lot like the **apparel** you wear. They go in and out of **style**. Do you know anyone named Michael or Jessica? Many Americans born in the 1980s and 1990s have these names. These names are in **fashion** today.

Styles change less **frequently** for boys' names than for girls' names. The name Michael has been a top **favorite** for 100 years. Matthew, David, and Daniel have also been used for most of the **century**. Tyler and Zachary were in style 100 years ago.

"Our names were popular 100 years ago."

Girls seem to have more **choices** in names. Today Aliza, Keisha, Lauren, and Emily are **quite** popular. Names such as Sarah, Amanda, and Elizabeth were **prevalent** a century ago. And they are favorites again today. What girls' names were used often when your parents were your age? The favorites for girls were Carol, Nancy, Debbie, and Linda.

More Americans used to have the same first names. Now many parents try to choose **unique** names. They want to be sure their child will be the only one around with that name.

GETTING THE DETAILS

Which of the following is not among the most popular names today?

Check the best answer.

____ Michael

____ Jessica

____ Debbie

____ Lauren

ALPHABET IS TOP CHOICE FOR WORD ORDER

NEW WORDS

apparel
style
quite
fashion
frequently
favorite
century
prevalent
choices
unique

Write the New Words on the lines in alphabetical order.

1. _____

2. _____

3. _____

4. _____

5. _____

6. _____

7. _____

8. _____

9. _____

10. _____

WORDS AND MEANINGS MATCH UP PERFECTLY!

☞ **Context clues** are words in a sentence or phrase that help you understand the meaning of a word. Look for context clues to help you match each New Word with its meaning.

Write the correct letter on each line.

____ 1. apparel

____ 2. style

____ 3. quite

____ 4. fashion

____ 5. frequently

____ 6. favorite

____ 7. century

____ 8. prevalent

____ 9. choices

____ 10. unique

a. possibilities to be selected from

b. coverings for the body, usually made of fabric; clothing

c. widespread; common; preferred

d. particular way of living or doing things

e. a time period lasting 100 years

f. very or somewhat; rather

g. the current style, usually changes over time

h. the one preferred or liked best

i. often; repeatedly

j. highly unusual; rare

COMPLETED SENTENCES ARE EVERYBODY'S FAVORITE

Use New Words to complete these sentences.

1. What is the latest _____ in shoes?

2. Sneakers are _____ high on my list.

3. I like the _____ of the clothes today.

4. Usually I like to wear clothes that are _____ .

5. My sister finds it hard to make _____ about what to wear.

6. That colorful outfit is my _____ .

7. Cotton is a fabric that is _____ in clothing styles.

8. It has been used to make beautiful clothes for more than a _____ .

9. _____ that is made from silk is usually very expensive.

10. It _____ lasts for a long time, though.

NOTHING UNUSUAL ABOUT SUFFIXES

☞ A **suffix** is a word part that can be added to the end of a root word to change its meaning.

Root Word + Suffix = New Word

joy + ful   = joyful

Look at the words below. A suffix has been added to a root word to form each word.
Write the root word on the first line and the suffix on the other.

Root Word	Root Word + Suffix	Suffix
_____	actor	_____
_____	artist	_____
_____	singer	_____
_____	collector	_____
_____	fisher	_____
_____	cartoonist	_____
_____	inventor	_____
_____	player	_____

MIXED-UP WORDS NEED HELP

Unscramble the New Words.

1. quineu _____

2. paprale _____

3. tenlavrep _____

4. yelst _____

5. vaorfeti _____

6. uteiq _____

7. hsoinaf _____

8. requyneltf _____

9. etnuyrc _____

10. icosech _____

NEW WORDS
apparel
style
quite
fashion
frequently
favorite
century
prevalent
choices
unique

"NAME THE MASCOT" CONTEST

 Pretend that there is a contest to name a mascot for your school. Write five sentences to convince your principal to use the name that you picked.

These questions will help guide your writing:

• What does the mascot look like?

• What does the mascot do?

• Why is the name you chose appropriate for a mascot for your school?

Use at least four New Words in your writing.

MOHAMMED WINS WORLDWIDE

Around the world, the most popular first name for a boy is Mohammed.

GIRLS TAKE BOYS' NAMES

In the 1800s, Ashley and Courtney were two of the top boys' names. Today they are two of the top girls' names.

READ MORE ABOUT IT

• *Remarkable Names of Real People* by John Train. (Clarkson N. Potter, 1977)

• *The Book of African Names* by Molefi Kete Asante. (Africa World Press, 1991)

• *Turtle Knows Your Name* by Ashley Bryon. (Atheneum, 1989)

You are ready for the test!

IMPROVE YOUR SCORE

When looking for a word that means the same as another, don't be fooled by a choice that means the opposite.

Read each group of words. Select the word or words that mean the __same__ as the underlined word. Fill in the circle for the answer at the bottom of the page.

1 visited <u>frequently</u>

   A seldom
   B often
   C never
   D once

2 made smart <u>choices</u>

   A acts of choosing
   B acts of giving
   C answers
   D remarks

3 <u>prevalent</u> ideas

   A rare
   B common
   C smart
   D wise

4 wear new <u>apparel</u>

   A hats
   B shoes
   C clothing
   D glasses

5 chose my <u>favorite</u>

   A one liked the least
   B one liked the best
   C one seen the most
   D one that is funniest

6 in the last <u>century</u>

   A year
   B 10 years
   C 50 years
   D 100 years

7 <u>quite</u> a fan

   A wealth
   B popular
   C really
   D somewhat

8 a name in <u>style</u>

   A favorite
   B choices
   C prevalent
   D fashion

Read each set of sentences. Select the word that completes the first sentence according to the stated meaning. Fill in the circle for the answer at the bottom of the page.

9 This dress was in ____ ten years ago. Which word indicates that this kind of dress was popular ten years ago?

   A apparel   **C** favorite
   B style   **D** prevalent

10 Mark is ____ interested in becoming a teacher. Which word indicates that Mark is very interested in becoming a teacher?

   A still   **C** quiet
   B quite   **D** not

11 What is the latest ____ today? Which word indicates the up-to-date way of dressing, acting, and behaving?

   A century   **C** apparel
   B fashion   **D** favorite

12 Her first name is ____ . Which word indicates that her first name is one-of-a-kind?

   A unkind   **C** unique
   B united   **D** union

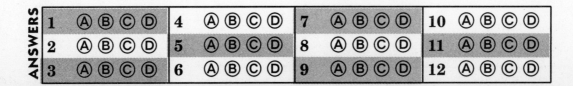

ANSWERS

1	Ⓐ Ⓑ Ⓒ Ⓓ	4	Ⓐ Ⓑ Ⓒ Ⓓ	7	Ⓐ Ⓑ Ⓒ Ⓓ	10	Ⓐ Ⓑ Ⓒ Ⓓ
2	Ⓐ Ⓑ Ⓒ Ⓓ	5	Ⓐ Ⓑ Ⓒ Ⓓ	8	Ⓐ Ⓑ Ⓒ Ⓓ	11	Ⓐ Ⓑ Ⓒ Ⓓ
3	Ⓐ Ⓑ Ⓒ Ⓓ	6	Ⓐ Ⓑ Ⓒ Ⓓ	9	Ⓐ Ⓑ Ⓒ Ⓓ	12	Ⓐ Ⓑ Ⓒ Ⓓ

22

AFRICAN AMERICAN COWBOYS HELP TAME THE WILD WEST

I t is after the Civil War. The slaves are free and are looking for jobs. Where can they go to start a new life?

Many **former** slaves headed west. When these African Americans got to the West, they easily found jobs on the wide-open **range**. There was a great need for cowboys to **tend** the **cattle** that roamed the plains. There wasn't time to train people to become cowboys. What the West needed was experienced cowhands.

African Americans were **valued** as cowboys because they knew how to handle horses and cattle from working on plantations. In fact, one out of every four cowboys in the West was African American.

The cowboys tended the cattle night and day, rescuing them from **quicksand**, mud, and **barbwire**. The cowboys were also **responsible** for **driving** the cattle hundreds of miles from the ranches to the railroad stations. Brave African American cowboys played a big part in helping **tame** the Wild West.

MAIN IDEA FOUND IN STORY

What is this story mainly about?

Check the best answer.

○ the Civil War

○ African American cowboys

○ the life of a cowboy

○ former slaves who trained others to become cowboys

ALPHABET KEEPS WORDS IN ORDER

Write the New Words on the lines in alphabetical order.

NEW WORDS

former

range

tend

cattle

valued

quicksand

barbwire

responsible

driving

tame

1. _____   6. _____

2. _____   7. _____

3. _____   8. _____

4. _____   9. _____

5. _____   10. _____

WORDS AND MEANINGS TEND TO MATCH

☞ **Context clues** are words in a sentence or phrase that help you understand the meaning of a word. Look for context clues to help you match each New Word with its meaning.

Write the correct letter on each line.

____ 1. former   a. leading or forcing to go in a certain direction

____ 2. range   b. a large open grazing area for cattle and livestock

____ 3. tend   c. overcome the wildness of; make gentle

____ 4. cattle   d. watch over; take care of

____ 5. valued   e. loose, wet sand not firm enough to stand on

____ 6. quicksand   f. cows and bulls

____ 7. barbwire   g. given much importance; highly thought of

____ 8. responsible   h. wire with sharp points along it, used for fences or barriers

____ 9. driving   i. past; earlier

____ 10. tame   j. held accountable for; in charge of

COMPLETE SENTENCES VALUED BY READERS

Use New Words to complete these sentences.

NEW WORDS

driving

range

cattle

valued

quicksand

former

barbwire

responsible

tend

tame

1. I met my _____ teacher, Mrs. Jones, at the store.

2. Before the West was settled, the buffalo _____ spread out for miles.

3. Sometimes my parents ask me to _____ to my little sister.

4. My uncle tended _____ on a ranch.

5. Good study habits are _____ at my school.

6. Hikers should always be careful not to step in _____ .

7. _____ is a good way to keep farm animals from wandering.

8. My sister and I are _____ for cleaning our own rooms.

9. In England, farmers use dogs for _____ sheep out to pasture and back.

10. The animal trainer worked to _____ the wild horse.

ROOT WORDS REFORM, FORM NEW WORDS

A **root word** is a word that is used as a base for making other words. For example, the root word for <u>unsuccessful</u> is <u>success</u>. The **prefix** <u>un</u> and the **suffix** <u>ful</u> were added to make a new word.

Circle the root of each word below.

1. darkness
2. inactive
3. northward
4. misspelled
5. formerly
6. enclosed
7. recounting
8. unneeded

9. painter
10. nonfiction
11. untamed
12. ungraceful
13. exchange
14. unbreakable
15. unmusical
16. yearly

17. misused
18. untended
19. encircled
20. slowest
21. disappear
22. friendship
23. midday
24. recalling

CAN YOU TAME THE WILD PUZZLE?

Use New Words to finish the crossword puzzle.

NEW WORDS

former	quicksand
range	responsible
tend	barbwire
cattle	driving
valued	tame

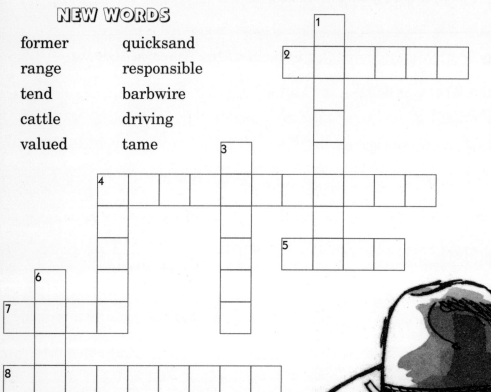

ACROSS

2. cows and bulls
4. in charge of
5. take care of
7. make gentle
8. loose, wet sand
9. leading in a certain direction

DOWN

1. wire with sharp points on it
3. past
4. grazing area for cattle
6. given much importance

HAT CHAT

American cowboys got the idea for cowboy hats when they saw the wide hats Mexican cowboys wore.

THE MOST FAMOUS AFRICAN AMERICAN COWBOYS OF THEM ALL

Do you know who some of the most famous African American cowboys were? Do some research with a partner to find out. Then write a short report. Use an encyclopedia or other books for information.

These questions will help guide your writing:

- What were the cowboys' names and where were they born?
- How did they become cowboys?
- What were some of their adventures?

Use at least four New Words in your report.

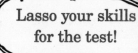

Lasso your skills for the test!

READING ROUNDUP

- *Cowboys* by L. Matthews. (Rourke, 1992)
- *Cowboys of the Wild West* by Russell Freedman. (Ticknor & Fields, 1985)
- *Reflections of a Black Cowboy: Book One—Cowboys* by Robert Miller. (Silver Burdett Press, 1991)
- *Reflections of a Black Cowboy: Book Two—The Buffalo Soldiers* by Robert Miller. (Silver Burdett Press, 1991)

SECRETS TO SUCCESS ON TESTS

If you skip a question in the test, be sure to skip that line in the answer box.

Complete each definition with the best word or words. Fill in the circle for the answer at the bottom of the page.

1 Cows, bulls, steers, and oxen are called . . . .

   A range   **C** cattle
   B tame   **D** cowboys

2 To have thought highly of is to have . . . .

   A valued   **C** tend
   B range   **D** barbed

3 A wet and loose kind of dirt in which a heavy object can be trapped is . . . .

   A quicksilver   **C** quicklime
   B quicksand   **D** quicken

4 A person who is accountable for something is . . . .

   A driving   **C** tame
   B responsible **D** former

5 To make something or someplace easier to manage is to . . . .

   A tend   **C** tan
   B tame   **D** tap

6 Because of its sharp points, the wire used on the range was called . . . .

   A driving   **C** range
   B cattle   **D** barbwire

7 To watch over is to . . . .

   A tame   **C** range
   B tend   **D** roam

8 Open land where cattle graze is called the . . . .

   A quicksand   **C** range
   B plantation   **D** Wild West

Read each sentence. Select the answer that best completes each one. Fill in the circle for the answer at the bottom of the page.

9 The cows were grazing on the ____ .

   A cattle   **C** quicksand
   B range   **D** mud

10 The cowboys were responsible for ____ the cattle to the railroad stations.

   A rescuing   **C** driving
   B keeping   **D** working

11 Cowboys had to ____ the cattle to keep them from harm.

   A range   **C** tame
   B tend   **D** free

12 Many African American cowboys were ____ slaves.

   A valued   **C** working
   B responsible **D** former

ANSWERS

1	Ⓐ Ⓑ Ⓒ Ⓓ	4	Ⓐ Ⓑ Ⓒ Ⓓ	7	Ⓐ Ⓑ Ⓒ Ⓓ	10	Ⓐ Ⓑ Ⓒ Ⓓ
2	Ⓐ Ⓑ Ⓒ Ⓓ	5	Ⓐ Ⓑ Ⓒ Ⓓ	8	Ⓐ Ⓑ Ⓒ Ⓓ	11	Ⓐ Ⓑ Ⓒ Ⓓ
3	Ⓐ Ⓑ Ⓒ Ⓓ	6	Ⓐ Ⓑ Ⓒ Ⓓ	9	Ⓐ Ⓑ Ⓒ Ⓓ	12	Ⓐ Ⓑ Ⓒ Ⓓ

ROBOTS EASE WORK WOES

A robot is an **automatic** machine. It can do the work of several people. Robots are often **controlled** by a computer. The computer **instructs** the robots to do long and **complicated** jobs. As workers, robots have a lot going for them. They don't get **weary**, make mistakes, or take vacations. They don't get bored either, even with **dull** work.

We often think of robots as mechanical people. Some can look like an arm. You see this type of robot in an automatic car wash. These robot arms spray the car with water and brush off the dirt. Other robot arms are used in factories. They may **assemble** cars or fill cans and bottles.

Robots are also important in **exploring** space. Since they don't need food, air, or comfort, they can work where astronauts cannot.

In the **future**, robots may help in your school. Perhaps they may be in many homes, too, just as computers are today. Think about it. Couldn't you use a robot for your **chores**?

STORY EXPLORERS FIND MAIN IDEA

What is this story mainly about?

Check the best answer.

○ Robots look like mechanical people or arms.

○ Robots can work for people.

○ Robots are never tired.

○ Robots are important in exploring space.

ALPHABET MAKES WORD ORDER AUTOMATIC

Write the New Words in alphabetical order.

NEW WORDS

exploring
automatic
complicated
assemble
chores
instructs
dull
controlled
weary
future

1. _____

2. _____

3. _____

4. _____

5. _____

6. _____

7. _____

8. _____

9. _____

10. _____

WORDS ARE MEANING MACHINES

Use context clues or the glossary to match each New Word below with its meaning. Write the correct letter on each line.

____ 1. assemble

____ 2. complicated

____ 3. weary

____ 4. instructs

____ 5. automatic

____ 6. chores

____ 7. controlled

____ 8. exploring

____ 9. future

____ 10. dull

a. tired; worn out

b. not interesting; boring

c. ruled, guided, or managed

d. time that is to come; time after the present time

e. to put together the parts of

f. moving or working by itself

g. the act of traveling in a region that is not well-known to find out more about it

h. not simple

i. gives information; teaches

j. common tasks that have to be done

INCOMPLETE SENTENCES DO NOT COMPUTE

Finish these sentences. Write a New Word on each line.

1. James finished all his _____ by five o'clock.

2. He was too _____ to play football with his brothers.

3. Our school installed _____ lights in the schoolyard.

4. The lights are now _____ by a computer.

5. Please help me _____ this new wagon.

6. The directions are too _____ for me to understand.

7. It was a _____ , rainy afternoon.

8. Andy thought that _____ his grandmother's treasure-filled attic would be fun.

9. The teacher _____ the class to study hard.

10. They will be taking the test in the near _____ .

NEW WORDS
automatic
complicated
exploring
chores
controlled
weary
assemble
instructs
future
dull

PREFIXES MAKE WORD CONNECTIONS

☞ A **prefix** is a word part that can be added to the beginning of a root word. Adding a prefix changes the meaning of the root word.

The prefix **re** means <u>again</u>.
The prefix **dis** means <u>opposite of</u>.

Add the prefix <u>re</u> or <u>dis</u> to each underlined word. Write the new word on the line.

1. <u>assemble</u> again _____

2. opposite of <u>comfort</u> _____

3. <u>work</u> again _____

4. <u>fill</u> again _____

5. opposite of <u>order</u> _____

6. opposite of <u>connect</u> _____

7. <u>count</u> again _____

8. opposite of <u>approve</u> _____

WORD SEARCH SOON TO BE UNDER CONTROL

Find each New Word in the word search and circle it. The words may appear vertically, horizontally, or diagonally.

```
C H D O R E M A F T I C E
D D U L L W E R U R Y H X
C O M P L I C A T E D O P
E D I S O L T R U C T R L
T R N C O M P W R C O E O
W A S S E M B L E U C S R
S A T U T R E X L A I C I
L O R E T R P E D O R E N
L D U L R L M P U T E Y G
I N C C O N T R O L L E D
M R T R U T E D L I C A O
C O S C N T R L M B L E T
M A U T O M A T I C T O R
```

DID YOU KNOW?

- The word *robot* was coined by the Czech playwright Karel Capek in 1921 in his play, *R.U.R.* (*Rossum's Universal Robots*).
- The idea of mechanical creatures has been around for a long time. A man-made bronze servant appears in the *Iliad*, by the ancient Greek poet Homer. And it is said that Leonardo da Vinci made a mechanical lion that walked and roared.

READ MORE ABOUT IT

- *Robots: What They Are, What They Do* by Fredericka Berger. (Greenwillow, 1992)
- *Ready-Set-Robot* by Lilian Hoban. (Harper and Row, 1982)
- *Robots: Your High-Tech World* by Gloria Skurzynski. (Bradbury Press, 1990)

ROBOT STORY REVEALS KID/COMPUTER CONNECTION

 Imagine that you just discovered this robot in your basement or garage. Write a story about what you would do with it.

These questions will help guide your writing:

- What can the robot do?
- How do you feel about the robot?
- What happens when you show it to your friends or family?

Use at least four New Words in your story.

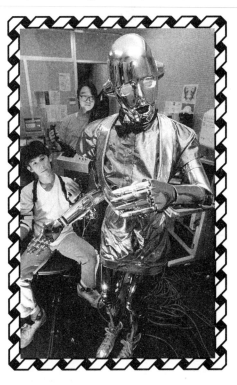

You are programmed for the test!

SECRETS TO SUCCESS ON TESTS

Relax! If you are nervous, take a few deep breaths before you begin.

Read each group of words. Select the word or words that mean the <u>opposite</u> of the underlined word. Fill in the circle for the answer at the bottom of the page.

1 a <u>complicated</u> problem

    A unusual   **C** not simple
    B easy   **D** not solved

2 car of the <u>future</u>

    A past   **C** present time
    B time to come   **D** tomorrow

3 a <u>dull</u> movie

    A boring   **C** long
    B funny   **D** exciting

4 feeling <u>weary</u>

    A used up   **C** lively
    B tired   **D** worn out

Read each set of sentences. Select the word that completes the first sentence according to the stated meaning. Fill in the circle for the answer at the bottom of the page.

5 Most washers that are used today are _____ machines. Which word indicates that the washers run by themselves?

    A complicated   **C** controlled
    B automatic   **D** dull

6 I _____ the car on the icy road. Which word means that the speaker guided the car?

    A controlled   **C** crashed
    B slid   **D** backed

7 When you finish your _____, you can go out and play. Which word means jobs around the house?

    A games   **C** tools
    B meals   **D** chores

8 _____ caves can be dangerous if you don't know what you are doing. Which word means traveling in an unknown area?

    A Complicated   **C** Exploring
    B Automatic   **D** Dull

9 The store will _____ the bike for a fee. Which word means that the store will put the parts together for you?

    A assign   **C** assemble
    B assure   **D** assist

10 The teacher _____ the students. Which word means that the teacher passes on knowledge to the students?

    A weary   **C** fills
    B instructs   **D** feeds

11 Driving a car is a _____ skill. Which word means that there is much to learn to be able to drive a car?

    A complicated   **C** dull
    B future   **D** automatic

12 I felt _____ after a long day's work. Which word indicates that the speaker was tired?

    A dull   **C** weary
    B controlled   **D** complicated

ANSWERS

1 Ⓐ Ⓑ Ⓒ Ⓓ	4 Ⓐ Ⓑ Ⓒ Ⓓ	7 Ⓐ Ⓑ Ⓒ Ⓓ	10 Ⓐ Ⓑ Ⓒ Ⓓ
2 Ⓐ Ⓑ Ⓒ Ⓓ	5 Ⓐ Ⓑ Ⓒ Ⓓ	8 Ⓐ Ⓑ Ⓒ Ⓓ	11 Ⓐ Ⓑ Ⓒ Ⓓ
3 Ⓐ Ⓑ Ⓒ Ⓓ	6 Ⓐ Ⓑ Ⓒ Ⓓ	9 Ⓐ Ⓑ Ⓒ Ⓓ	12 Ⓐ Ⓑ Ⓒ Ⓓ

ZAMBONI—MONSTER OF A MACHINE!

It's over seven feet wide, thirteen feet long, and six feet tall. It weighs more than three tons and has **studs** on its feet. It's not a monster. It's the Zamboni.

The Zamboni is the machine that cleans off the ice at an ice-skating **rink**. It glides over the ice, filling in grooves and **gouges**. A long **spiral** blade **shaves** off the top layer of ice, and then the Zamboni sprays hot water onto the ice. When the water freezes, the ice is **slick.**

The first Zamboni was made in California in 1949. The **inventor**, Frank J. Zamboni, used the machine to make the ice smooth in his ice-skating rink.

When the **owners** of other ice-skating rinks saw the new machine, they wanted one, too. So Frank J. Zamboni started a company to make and sell the **gigantic** machines. Soon many ice rinks had them, and the Zamboni became world famous.

So next time you go to a hockey game or go ice skating, look for a Zamboni **circling** the rink, smoothing the ice for the skaters.

FINDING MAIN IDEA IS NOT A SLICK TRICK

What is the main idea of this story?

Check the best answer.

❑ The Zamboni weighs more than three tons.

❑ The Zamboni is a machine for smoothing ice on skating rinks.

❑ The Zamboni is a dangerous machine.

❑ It is fun to drive a Zamboni.

ALPHABET PUTS WORDS ON ICE

Write the New Words in alphabetical order on the lines.

NEW WORDS

studs
rink
gouges
spiral
shaves
slick
inventor
owners
gigantic
circling

bank

_____

farm

_____

_____

hot

_____

night

_____

party

_____

sand

_____

_____

_____

WORDS AND MEANINGS MATCH

☞ **Context clues** are words in a sentence or phrase that help you understand the meaning of a word. Look for context clues to help you match each New Word with its meaning.

Write the correct letter on each line.

____ 1. spiral   a. moving around in a circle

____ 2. rink   b. raised knobs or projections used to prevent sliding on slippery surfaces

____ 3. shaves   c. the rightful possessors of something

____ 4. slick   d. an area for skating

____ 5. studs   e. cuts or grooves in smooth surfaces

____ 6. inventor   f. circling around a center in a curve

____ 7. owners   g. a person who devises a new tool or process

____ 8. gouges   h. removes thin layers by cutting

____ 9. circling   i. slippery and wet; smooth

____ 10. gigantic   j. huge; immense; very large

34

SENTENCE GOUGES GONE
NEW WORDS FILL IN SENTENCE HOLES

Use New Words to complete these sentences.

1. Football players wear shoes with _____ for better traction.

2. I would rather skate at a _____ than on a pond.

3. Sculptors use chisels to make _____ in stone.

4. My aunt's new house has a _____ staircase.

5. My older brother _____ his face every day.

6. The speeding car skidded on the _____ , icy road.

7. Thomas Edison was a brilliant _____ .

8. Phyllis and Evelyn are the _____ of their own company.

9. I was afraid to ride that _____ horse.

10. In our solar system, the planets are always _____ the sun.

UNDERSTANDING ANTONYMS

☞ **Antonyms** are words that have opposite meanings.

large and **small**   **cold** and **hot**

Find a word from the Word List that is an antonym for each puzzle word. Write the words in the boxes.

4. C O P I E R

3. R E N T E R S

1. S M A L L

6. B U M P S

7. T I M I D

5. S T I C K Y

2. P R O M O T E

8. B E T T E R

WORD LIST

oppose
bold
gouges
worse
slick
inventor
owners
gigantic

CATEGORIES ARE REALLY GIGANTIC WORD GROUPS

 A **category** is a group to which similar things belong.

Bears, **lions**, and **zebras** belong to the category <u>wild animals</u>.

Circle the three words that belong in each category.

1. things that are <u>shaved</u>

   ice   face

   river   wood

2. things that are <u>slick</u>

   ice   soap

   wax   tree

3. great <u>inventors</u>

   William Shakespeare

   Thomas Edison

   George Washington Carver

   The Wright Brothers

4. <u>gigantic</u> things

   mountain   skyscraper

   dinosaur   mouse

5. things with <u>studs</u>

   shoe   family

   tire   Zamboni

6. <u>circling</u> things

   merry-go-round   planet

   gouges   moon

I DIDN'T KNOW THAT

○ Watch out! Zambonis don't have brakes. Instead, the driver uses a lever called a throttle to control the speed of the machine. When the driver pushes the throttle forward, the Zamboni goes faster. When the driver pulls back on the throttle, the Zamboni slows down or stops. Airplanes have throttles, too. And so do trains.

○ The Upper Deck sports card company thought so much of the Zamboni that they issued a commemorative card in its honor.

READ ALL ABOUT IT

- *Ice Skating* by Tim Wood. (Franklin Watts, 1990)
- *World's Strangest Hockey Stories* by Bart Rockwell. (Watermill Press, 1993)

WATCH:

- *Magic Memories on Ice.* (CBS Fox Video Sports, 1989)

TAKING THE RIDE OF YOUR LIFE

Imagine that you could drive a Zamboni and clean off the ice during the intermission of a skating competition. Write a paragraph about your experience.

These questions will help guide your writing:

- What did it feel like to drive the Zamboni on the ice?
- What did the ice look like before and after you cleaned it?
- What did the people in the stands do as you cleaned the ice?

Use at least four New Words in your writing.

Get a perfect score on the test!

TEST-TAKING SECRETS REVEALED

Look for hints in the sentence to help you understand the meaning of a word.

Read each sentence. Select the answer that best completes each one. Fill in the circle for the answer at the bottom of the page.

1 There were deep ____ in the ice from too much use.

    A shaves   **C** gouges
    B studs   **D** owners

2 The ____ on the Zamboni help it to grip the ice as it drives over it.

    A shaves   **C** owners
    B gouges   **D** studs

3 The ____ movement of the blade removes a layer of ice.

    A spiral   **C** shaves
    B slippery   **D** slick

4 Who are the ____ of these lost articles?

    A studs   **C** gouges
    B owners   **D** shaves

5 The airplane spent a half hour ____ the airport.

    A circling   **C** shaving
    B smoothing   **D** cleaning

6 The Zamboni ____ the old layer of ice and makes a new one.

    A gouges   **C** shaves
    B studs   **D** shoves

7 Be careful of the ____ sidewalk.

    A spiral   **C** gigantic
    B circling   **D** slick

8 He was overwhelmed because he won a ____ prize.

    A circling   **C** gigantic
    B spiral   **D** rink

Read the paragraph. Select the words that best fit in the blanks. Fill in the circles for the answers at the bottom of the page.

The Zamboni is named after its __9__. It is a __10__ machine for tending the ice in a __11__. When the Zamboni finishes with the ice, it is so __12__ you can see your face in it.

9 **A** owners   **C** inventor
     B blade   **D** monster

10 **A** spiral   **C** circling
     B rink   **D** gigantic

11 **A** spiral   **C** slick
     B rink   **D** gouges

12 **A** slick   **C** gigantic
     B spiral   **D** circling

ANSWERS

1	Ⓐ Ⓑ Ⓒ Ⓓ	4	Ⓐ Ⓑ Ⓒ Ⓓ	7	Ⓐ Ⓑ Ⓒ Ⓓ	10	Ⓐ Ⓑ Ⓒ Ⓓ
2	Ⓐ Ⓑ Ⓒ Ⓓ	5	Ⓐ Ⓑ Ⓒ Ⓓ	8	Ⓐ Ⓑ Ⓒ Ⓓ	11	Ⓐ Ⓑ Ⓒ Ⓓ
3	Ⓐ Ⓑ Ⓒ Ⓓ	6	Ⓐ Ⓑ Ⓒ Ⓓ	9	Ⓐ Ⓑ Ⓒ Ⓓ	12	Ⓐ Ⓑ Ⓒ Ⓓ

37

GROWLING STOMACH DISTURBS CLASS

"My stomach is growling. I hope it doesn't bite."

The classroom is quiet as you and the other students are writing in your journals. Lunch is in ten minutes. "Today is pizza day," you think. "Am I **starved**!" Then you hear the sound. G-R-O-W-L. The sound seems to have come from your **stomach**. Your classmates giggle. Feeling **embarrassed**, you wonder, "Why is my stomach **growling**?"

Believe it or not, you hear this noise because your stomach is working as it should. Your stomach is a powerful muscle that is always **creating** digestive **juices**. It churns the juices together with the food in the stomach. When your stomach has sent its food to the **intestines**, air **combines** with the digestive juices and food, which has now become a liquid. As the air and liquid **squirt** through your long, winding intestines, they turn corners and go back and forth and up and down. All that churning and turning through a small area makes a **gurgling** noise. As you can see, a better name for a *growling stomach* would be *growling intestines*.

MAIN IDEA UNCOVERED

What is this story mainly about?

Check the best answer.

- ⭕ growling intestines that begin to bark
- ⭕ why your stomach growls
- ⭕ what happens to your stomach on pizza day
- ⭕ how to avoid a growling stomach

ALPHABET KEEPS WORDS IN ORDER

Write the New Words in alphabetical order.

caring

_____

_____

_____

formula

_____

_____

_____

salivate

_____

_____

New Words

growling

starved

embarrassed

juices

squirt

combines

intestines

creating

gurgling

stomach

OF ALL THE NERVE

Nerve endings in your stomach tell your brain if you are hungry.

MEANINGS REVEALED

☞ **Context clues** are words in a sentence or phrase that help you understand the meaning of a word. Look for context clues to help you match each New Word with its meaning.

Write the correct letter on each line.

_____ 1. growling   a. deprived of food

_____ 2. squirt   b. liquids

_____ 3. creating   c. making or bringing something into being

_____ 4. starved   d. a muscular organ connected to the esophagus that digests food

_____ 5. stomach   e. feeling self-conscious or uncomfortable

_____ 6. juices   f. making a rumbling, menacing sound

_____ 7. gurgling   g. to force or shoot a liquid in a narrow stream

_____ 8. embarrassed   h. the long, winding organs of digestion

_____ 9. combines   i. making a bubbling or rippling sound

_____10. intestines   j. brings together; joins; unites

MISSING WORDS FOUND

Finish these sentences. Write a New Word on each line.

1. The _____ infant is content in her father's arms.

2. I _____ the lemon onto my salad.

3. After eating a whole batch of cookies, Debbie's _____ ached.

4. When her mother found the empty cookie carton on the kitchen table, Debbie was _____ .

5. The _____ dog frightened the children.

6. Thin, almost _____ , and dirty, the animal would not let anyone near the scraps of food.

7. The biology professor presented a video showing how food _____ with acids in the digestive tract.

8. He also taught the class about the construction of the large and small _____ .

9. The chef squeezed the _____ of fresh oranges and lemons to make a tangy drink.

10. _____ healthy meals was very important to her.

New Words

growling

starved

embarrassed

juices

squirt

combines

intestines

creating

gurgling

stomach

SOLVE THE HOMONYM PUZZLE

Homonyms are words that sound alike but have different meanings and spellings.

sea and **see**   **plate** and **plait**

Draw lines to match the homonyms below.

1. peace   hole
2. feet   piece
3. seam   sun
4. whole   feat
5. son   seem
6. soar   bored
7. weight   weak
8. pale   wait
9. board   pail
10. week   sore

Use the homonyms to the left to complete these sentences.

11. The _____ of the snow bent the shrub in our front yard.

12. The former enemies signed an agreement with the hope of achieving _____ .

13. Tom was _____ after waiting a whole hour for the bus.

14. The _____ of her skirt got caught in the car door.

15. All the _____ members approved of the office manager.

16. On a trip to Wyoming, we saw a bald eagle _____ through the afternoon sky.

17. Orange cones encircled the _____ in the middle of the street.

18. Mary's _____ hurt when she walked barefoot over the hot stones.

19. Juan was _____ and tired from his bout with the flu.

20. Jo was upset because we left only one _____ of candy.

DON'T GET YOUR SIGNALS CROSSED

Use the New Words to finish the crossword puzzle.

ACROSS

2. making something
4. bubbling
5. organ connected to the esophagus
6. to shoot in a jet
8. uncomfortable
9. very hungry

DOWN

1. menacing sound
2. mixes
3. liquids from fruits or vegetables
7. long, winding organs of the body

YOU ARE WHAT YOU EAT

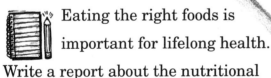

Eating the right foods is important for lifelong health. Write a report about the nutritional needs of someone your age. Use an encyclopedia or other books to find information.

These questions will help guide your writing:

- What types of foods should be eaten to maintain proper health?
- What foods aid digestion?
- What foods are bad for your health?

Use at least four of the New Words in your report.

MORE INFORMATION TO DIGEST

Read:

- *Body Noises: Where They Come From and Why They Happen* by Susan Kovacs Buxbaum and Rita Golden Gelman. (Knopf, 1983)

- *Outside-in* by Clare Smallman. (Barron's, 1986)

TONGUE TWISTER

The scientific name for stomach-growling is *borborygmi.*

Save room for the test!

SCORE HIGHER ON TESTS

Never leave an answer blank. Think about the question and make your very best guess.

Read each set of sentences. Select the word or words that best complete the second sentence in each set. Fill in the circle for the answer at the bottom of the page.

1 The gurgling water kept me awake all night. Gurgling means having a—

  A bubbling sound   **C** banging sound
  B loud noise   **D** running noise

2 By dinner time, I felt as if I was starved. Starved means very—

  A tired   **C** weak
  B hungry   **D** angry

3 His stomach was full from eating a big meal. A stomach is the human organ that—

  A keeps the blood moving
  B receives the swallowed food
  C helps a person to see
  D allows a person to think

4 Your intestines are attached to your stomach. Intestines are the human organs that—

  A keep the blood moving
  B receive the swallowed food
  C help a person to walk
  D finish the digestion of food

5 I was embarrassed because my homework was not finished. Embarrassed means feeling—

  A sick   **C** uncomfortable
  B tired   **D** angry

6 The machine is creating a lot of noise. Creating means—

  A bringing into being
  B changing
  C cranking out
  D clanking

7 Liquids squirt through the intestines making a gurgling sound. Squirt means—

  A shoot in a narrow stream
  B move in fits and starts
  C push along
  D pour in a steady flow

8 Hot air combines with moisture to form steam. Combines means—

  A separates   **C** disappears
  B stands   **D** joins

Read each group of words. Select the word that means the same as the underlined word. Fill in the circle for the answer at the bottom of the page.

9 combines with oxygen

  A joins   **C** growls
  B flows   **D** works

10 squirt from the bottle

  A pour   **C** spurt
  B drip   **D** flow

11 my growling stomach

  A hungry   **C** sick
  B empty   **D** gurgling

12 digestive juices

  A fuels   **C** liquids
  B gases   **D** solids

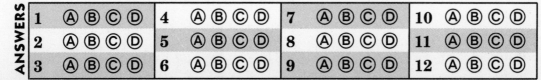

ANSWERS

1 Ⓐ Ⓑ Ⓒ Ⓓ	4 Ⓐ Ⓑ Ⓒ Ⓓ	7 Ⓐ Ⓑ Ⓒ Ⓓ	10 Ⓐ Ⓑ Ⓒ Ⓓ
2 Ⓐ Ⓑ Ⓒ Ⓓ	5 Ⓐ Ⓑ Ⓒ Ⓓ	8 Ⓐ Ⓑ Ⓒ Ⓓ	11 Ⓐ Ⓑ Ⓒ Ⓓ
3 Ⓐ Ⓑ Ⓒ Ⓓ	6 Ⓐ Ⓑ Ⓒ Ⓓ	9 Ⓐ Ⓑ Ⓒ Ⓓ	12 Ⓐ Ⓑ Ⓒ Ⓓ

CONDORS STRUGGLE TO SURVIVE

THESE BIG BIRDS ARE ON THE VERGE OF EXTINCTION

North America's largest bird may no longer be **soaring** in the warm California sky. Very few condors **remain** in the wild. This bird is in danger of becoming **extinct**.

The condor is special because of its size and **appearance**. Its wing spread can span ten feet. The bird has a **bald** yellow head and a hooked beak. Its eyes and neck are reddish. The condor's feathers are black and white.

There are several reasons for the condor's small numbers. Today fruit trees grow where cattle were once raised, leaving little food for the meat-eating condors. Hunters used the large bird for an easy **target**. Also, the condor lays only one egg every two years. If someone **approaches** its nest, the condor may not return to feed its young.

Laws now **protect** the condor. Land has been set aside for the bird to live safely. In April of 1985, the first California condor to hatch in a cage lived! Maybe someday with people's help the condor won't have to **struggle** for **survival**.

SEQUENCE KEEPS STORY ON TARGET

Which of these happened after cattle ranches were replaced with fruit trees?

Check the best answer.

○ The condor learned to eat fruit.
○ The condor's appearance changed.
○ Hunters began to shoot at the condor.
○ The condor had little to eat.

THE AMAZING ALPHABET

Write the New Words in alphabetical order.

apparent

_____

NEW WORDS

remain

bald

target   ball

soaring   extend

survival

approaches

struggle

extinct   provide

appearance

protect

soap

_____

strange

_____

tardy

WORDS AND MEANINGS MATCH

Use context clues or the glossary to match each New Word below with its meaning.

Write the correct letter on the line.

____ 1. approaches   a. the act or fact of continuing to exist

____ 2. bald   b. rising or flying in the air

____ 3. survival   c. to go on being; continue

____ 4. extinct   d. no longer living; having died out

____ 5. appearance   e. the way a person or thing looks

____ 6. struggle   f. having no hair on all or part of the scalp

____ 7. remain   g. a thing aimed at, as in shooting a rifle or arrow

____ 8. soaring   h. to guard or defend against harm or danger; shield

____ 9. target   i. comes closer or draws nearer

____ 10. protect   j. to try or work very hard; strive

WORDS FILL INCOMPLETE SENTENCES

Finish these sentences. Write a New Word on each line.

1. An _____ animal will never live again.

2. It has lost its fight for _____ .

3. We saw sea gulls _____ through the sky.

4. Sometimes they must _____ against very strong winds.

5. Paul played the part of a _____ man in our class play.

6. Having no hair really changed his _____ .

7. Carla aimed her arrow at the _____ .

8. She will _____ in first place after the second round

of shooting.

9. If the fire _____ our home, we will have to leave.

10. Then the firefighters will have to _____ our house.

MEANINGS CHANGE WITH SUFFIXES

👉 A **suffix** is a word part that can be added to the end of a root word. Adding a suffix changes the meaning of the word.

The suffixes **tion** and **ness** mean <u>state of being</u>.

Draw a line to match each word with its meaning.

1. extinction	a. state of being protected		6. relation	f. state of being happy
2. baldness	b. state of being sad		7. correction	g. state of being related
3. protection	c. state of being wild		8. kindness	h. state of being completed
4. wildness	d. state of being extinct		9. happiness	i. state of being corrected
5. sadness	e. state of being bald		10. completion	j. state of being kind

WORDS SCRAMBLE FOR MEANING

Unscramble these New Words and write them on the lines.

NEW WORDS

remain	target	survival	struggle	appearance
bald	soaring	approaches	extinct	protect

1. airngos _____

2. mieran _____

3. trgate _____

4. anrepacepa _____

5. dalb _____

6. etopcrt _____

7. nitxcte _____

8. oapchpares _____

9. selugrtg _____

10. rvlasuiv _____

DON'T SHOOT!
SPARE THE RARE CONDOR

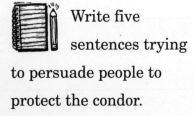 Write five sentences trying to persuade people to protect the condor.

These questions will help guide your writing:

- Why is the condor special?
- How can you show you care about the condor's survival?
- Why is it important to protect the condor?

Use at least four New Words in your sentences.

MORE SOARING FACTS ABOUT THE CONDOR

- The condor is the largest and heaviest flying bird in the world.
- The condor is a type of vulture.

READ MORE ABOUT IT

- *On the Brink of Extinction: The California Condor* by Caroline Arnold. (Harcourt Brace Jovanovich, 1993)
- *The Condor* by Lisa Westberg Peters. (Crestwood House, 1990)
- *Saving the Condor* by Nancy Schorsh. (Capstone Press, 1992)

Target your thoughts on the test!

TEST-DAY TIPS TOLD

Look over the entire test before you begin to see what you will be doing.

Read each group of words. Select the word or words that mean the same as the underlined word. Fill in the circle for the answer at the bottom of the page.

1 approaches the dog

   A   goes away from
   B   comes closer to
   C   takes care of
   D   goes along with

2 protect the money

   A   see
   B   carry
   C   guard
   D   spend

3 a bald head

   A   hairy
   B   hairless
   C   covered
   D   oval

4 an extinct animal

   A   died out
   B   ugly
   C   small
   D   wonderful

5 remain in the house

   A   work
   B   clean
   C   play
   D   stay

6 a soaring plane

   A   making noise
   B   having trouble
   C   flying upward
   D   flying downward

Complete each definition with the best word or words. Fill in the circle for the answer at the bottom of the page.

7 To struggle is to—

   A   run slowly
   B   try very hard
   C   put on clothes
   D   walk fast

8 A target is a—

   A   bird
   B   drawing
   C   thing aimed at
   D   thing that moves

9 The appearance of a thing is how it—

   A   looks
   B   sings
   C   talks
   D   walks

10 The survival of an animal is the act of—

   A   running away
   B   walking
   C   remaining alive
   D   thinking

11 To protect something is to—

   A   trade it
   B   sell it
   C   buy it
   D   defend it

12 To be extinct is to be—

   A   able to do something
   B   no longer living
   C   afraid of animals
   D   worried about school

ANSWERS

1	Ⓐ Ⓑ Ⓒ Ⓓ	4	Ⓐ Ⓑ Ⓒ Ⓓ	7	Ⓐ Ⓑ Ⓒ Ⓓ	10	Ⓐ Ⓑ Ⓒ Ⓓ
2	Ⓐ Ⓑ Ⓒ Ⓓ	5	Ⓐ Ⓑ Ⓒ Ⓓ	8	Ⓐ Ⓑ Ⓒ Ⓓ	11	Ⓐ Ⓑ Ⓒ Ⓓ
3	Ⓐ Ⓑ Ⓒ Ⓓ	6	Ⓐ Ⓑ Ⓒ Ⓓ	9	Ⓐ Ⓑ Ⓒ Ⓓ	12	Ⓐ Ⓑ Ⓒ Ⓓ

OLD FOSSILS GIVE VISITORS A FRIGHT

illions of years ago **swamps** covered the land. Giant animals **roamed** through the **shallow** water and ate plants that grew very thick. These **monsters** are called dinosaurs.

We can **imagine** how these dinosaurs looked because their bones have been found and put back together. The bones show us that there were many kinds of dinosaurs.

Among the giants was the brontosaurus. This plant-eater grew to be 80 feet long and stood on four, **stout** legs. The tyrannosaurus rex was the largest meat-eater. Its teeth were six inches long. You can imagine the **fright** of the other dinosaurs when tyrannosaurus ran at them! The **shield** that grew behind the neck of the triceratops helped it defend itself from **attacks**. The triceratops usually had three horns and grew to be 25 feet long.

We can only guess why these giants became extinct. If you enjoy being scared, visit a **museum** that has dinosaur bones. Stand before one like the tyrannosaurus and picture it coming to life.

IS EVERYTHING IN ORDER?

Put the following events in the correct order.

Number the sentences from 1 to 4.

____ Dinosaur bones were set up in museums.

____ Dinosaur bones were found and put back together.

____ Dinosaurs lived in swamps.

____ Dinosaurs became extinct.

ALPHABET KEEPS WORDS FROM ROAMING

Write the New Words in alphabetical order.

ashes

_____

attend

friend

shake

_____

month

muscle

mushroom

_____

stone

_____

swan

NEW WORDS

swamps	monsters
shallow	stout
museum	fright
roamed	shield
imagine	attacks

MATCH WORDS AND MEANINGS

Use context clues or the glossary to match each New Word with its meaning. Write the correct letter on the line.

____ 1. attacks

____ 2. shallow

____ 3. fright

____ 4. monsters

____ 5. swamps

____ 6. shield

____ 7. museum

____ 8. stout

____ 9. imagine

____ 10. roamed

a. not deep

b. traveled about with no special plan or purpose; wandered

c. huge animals or things

d. strong; sturdy; thick

e. to make up a picture or idea in the mind; form an idea of

f. a building or room for keeping and showing objects important in history, science, or art

g. sudden fear; alarm

h. pieces of wet or spongy land; marshes

i. actions against another that are intended to harm

j. something that guards or protects, as a safety guard over machinery

MISSING WORDS UNEARTHED
SENTENCES CAN NOW BE COMPLETED

Finish these sentences. Write a New Word on each line.

1. Our class went on a trip to the natural history _____ .

2. We saw a _____ used by the Vikings.

3. Kay jumped back and screamed in _____ .

4. "I thought _____ were chasing me!" she said.

5. In Florida there are large _____ .

6. There were reports of some _____ by alligators there.

7. Look in the mirror and _____ what you will look like in ten years.

8. Will you be short or tall, _____ or thin?

9. The young boy _____ too close to the swimming pool.

10. He is only allowed to go in the _____ wading pool.

SYLLABLES CUT MONSTER WORDS DOWN TO SIZE

☞ Words can be divided into smaller word parts, or **syllables**. For example, say the word popular and listen for its syllables.

pop u lar

Say each word and listen for the syllables. Then write the words on the lines, leaving spaces between the syllables.

Check a dictionary if you need help dividing the words.

1. shallow _____

2. imagine _____

3. monster _____

4. attack _____

5. museum _____

6. dinosaur _____

7. protect _____

8. giant _____

9. million _____

10. animal _____

ANALOGIES FORM MEANINGFUL RELATIONSHIPS

👉 **Analogies** show the relationship between things.

bird is to **nest** as **lion** is to **den**

sand is to **desert** as **ice** is to **glacier**

Complete the following analogies using the words in the list.

WORD LIST

shallow	monster	museum	run	pork
fright	swamp	smell	beginning	stout

---

1. <u>alligator</u> is to _____ as <u>frog</u> is to <u>pond</u>

2. <u>thin</u> is to <u>thick</u> as _____ is to <u>deep</u>

3. <u>scream</u> is to _____ as <u>cheer</u> is to <u>excitement</u>

4. _____ is to <u>scary</u> as <u>clown</u> is to <u>funny</u>

5. <u>paintings</u> is to _____ as <u>books</u> is to <u>library</u>

6. _____ is to <u>fat</u> as <u>tiny</u> is to <u>small</u>

7. <u>hear</u> is to <u>ears</u> as _____ is to <u>nose</u>

8. <u>pool</u> is to <u>swim</u> as <u>track</u> is to _____

9. <u>life</u> is to <u>death</u> as _____ is to <u>end</u>

10. _____ is to <u>pig</u> as <u>beef</u> is to <u>cow</u>

DIG THOSE DINOSAURS

• Dinosaurs roamed the earth for about 200 million years. Human beings have only existed for a fraction of that time.

• The sudden disappearance of the dinosaurs is still a mystery to scientists. Contrary to popular belief, however, many other kinds of creatures such as the sea crocodile also experienced mass extinction at about the same time.

READ MORE ABOUT IT

• *Dinosaur Dreams* by Allan Ahlberg. (Greenwillow, 1991)

• *Little Grunt and the Big Egg* by Tomie DePaola. (Holiday House, 1990)

THE LIFE AND TIMES OF A DINOSAUR

📝 Look at the picture of the dinosaur. Write a description about what you see and what you imagine.

These questions will help guide your writing:

• Where did the dinosaur make its home?

• How did the dinosaur act?

• What did the dinosaur eat?

Use at least four New Words in your sentences.

Take the test before you become extinct!

IMPROVE YOUR SCORE

Read all directions carefully. You may even want to read them a second time to make sure you understand them.

Read each sentence. Select the word that best completes each one. Fill in the circle for the answer at the bottom of the page.

1 I can imagine dinosaurs hiding in dark _____.

   A deserts
   B monsters
   C swamps
   D attacks

2 The soldier carried a _____ to protect him from the enemy's weapons.

   A shift
   B shape
   C share
   D shield

3 My bad dream filled me with _____.

   A fright
   B frill
   C fringe
   D freight

4 It is safe for you to wade in the _____ pond.

   A deep
   B stout
   C wide
   D shallow

5 _____ how surprised she will be to see you!

   A Repeat
   B Argue
   C Imagine
   D Retell

6 We _____ around the park for the rest of the afternoon.

   A crawled
   B slid
   C roamed
   D acted

Read each set of sentences. Select the word or words that best complete the second sentence in each set. Fill in the circle for the answer at the bottom of the page.

7 The little children were afraid of the scary <u>monster</u>. <u>Monster</u> means—

   A mask   **C** stuffed bear
   B story   **D** huge creature

8 We are going to see the art show at the <u>museum</u>. <u>Museum</u> means a building used for—

   A offices
   B school
   C keeping and lending books
   D displaying history, art, and science objects

9 The <u>stout</u> legs of the dinosaur were able to carry its heavy body. <u>Stout</u> means—

   A wild   **C** thin
   B thick   **D** short

10 The patriots began the <u>attacks</u> at midnight. <u>Attacks</u> means—

   A lesson   **C** vacation
   B show   **D** fight

11 The <u>fright</u> that I felt was caused by a strange noise. <u>Fright</u> means—

   A happiness   **C** fear
   B sadness   **D** surprise

12 Many different animals live in the <u>swamps</u> of Florida. <u>Swamps</u> means—

   A marshes   **C** valleys
   B deserts   **D** jungles

ANSWERS

1	Ⓐ Ⓑ Ⓒ Ⓓ	4	Ⓐ Ⓑ Ⓒ Ⓓ	7	Ⓐ Ⓑ Ⓒ Ⓓ	10	Ⓐ Ⓑ Ⓒ Ⓓ
2	Ⓐ Ⓑ Ⓒ Ⓓ	5	Ⓐ Ⓑ Ⓒ Ⓓ	8	Ⓐ Ⓑ Ⓒ Ⓓ	11	Ⓐ Ⓑ Ⓒ Ⓓ
3	Ⓐ Ⓑ Ⓒ Ⓓ	6	Ⓐ Ⓑ Ⓒ Ⓓ	9	Ⓐ Ⓑ Ⓒ Ⓓ	12	Ⓐ Ⓑ Ⓒ Ⓓ

STORYTELLER FOUND BURIED IN CLAY

The Cochiti Pueblo people of New Mexico are known for their beautiful **pottery**. Each Cochiti family makes pottery statues that look like their family **storyteller** telling stories to children. The children sit on the storyteller's lap. They look as if they are hanging on every word.

While they make pottery statues, the family **listens** to the family storyteller. The storyteller **shares** the Pueblo way of life. The storyteller is very **important** to the Cochiti. No written **records** of Cochiti history have been kept in the past. Storytellers have kept their history alive.

Making the pottery is a family affair. The freshly dug, rock-hard clay is first **soaked** in water. The soft clay is then **cleansed** of any sticks or stones. Sand is added for strength. Now the family plunges in, **molding** the clay. After the pottery is molded, it is left to dry. When it is dry, the pottery is sanded and then **polished** with a special stone. Then the pottery is painted and put into a kiln. The family waits and watches. At last the pottery is done.

THE TRUTH ABOUT COCHITI POTTERY

Which is <u>not</u> true about the making of Cochiti pottery?
Check the best answer.

____ The Cochiti model pottery after the family storyteller.

____ The Cochiti people have many written records of their history.

____ The clay used for making pottery is soaked in water to soften the clay.

____ The storyteller is an important part of the Cochiti culture.

THE AMAZING ALPHABET

Write the New Words in alphabetical order on the lines.

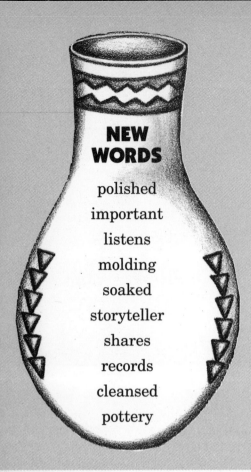

NEW WORDS

polished
important
listens
molding
soaked
storyteller
shares
records
cleansed
pottery

boat

_____

_____   _____

_____   _____

line   shale

_____   _____

_____   _____

paper   _____

MEANINGS BROUGHT TO LIGHT

☞ **Context clues** are words in a sentence or phrase that help you understand the meaning of a word. Look for context clues to help you match each New Word with its meaning.

Write the correct letter on each line.

____ 1. listens   a. forming or shaping

____ 2. important   b. removed of dirt or other impurities

____ 3. shares   c. accounts of activities and events

____ 4. records   d. significant or meaningful

____ 5. polished   e. person who tells histories, tales, and stories to others

____ 6. soaked   f. put in water or other liquid for a thorough wetting

____ 7. cleansed   g. hears and is alert to something in the environment

____ 8. molding   h. gives out knowledge, material, or other resources

____ 9. storyteller   i. made smooth and shiny

____ 10. pottery   j. dishes, pots, and bowls made of clay

MISSING WORDS RECOVERED

Finish these sentences. Write a New Word on each line.

1. The _____ came to share his experiences after the hurricane.

2. The woman _____ with interest to his tale.

3. The _____ were stored in the attic of the city hall.

4. Luckily they were not _____ or damaged when the building's sprinkling system went off.

5. Under the watchful eye of his mother, Tyrone _____ a candy bar with his younger sister.

6. She is happy that he has learned an _____ lesson.

7. The jeweler spent a great deal of time designing and _____ the silver bracelet.

8. The pin can be _____ with mild soap and water.

9. Grandmother keeps her silverware _____ .

10. She also dusts her _____ frequently.

THERE'S A NEW ENDING TO THIS WORD. . . WORKING WITH SUFFIXES

A **suffix** is a word part that can be added to the end of a root word. A suffix changes the meaning of the root word.

Ship can mean state of being, rank of, or skill as.

Need help? Look in your dictionary.

Add the suffix ship to the end of each word.

Write the new words on the lines.   *Now write the definitions of the new words you made.*

1. champion _____   11. _____

2. leader _____   12. _____

3. lord _____   13. _____

4. author _____   14. _____

5. kin _____   15. _____

6. professor _____   16. _____

7. horseman _____   17. _____

8. apprentice _____   18. _____

9. marksman _____   19. _____

10. sportsman _____   20. _____

WORDS LOST IN A SEA OF LETTERS!

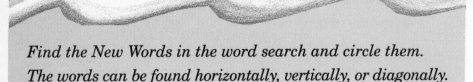

Find the New Words in the word search and circle them.
The words can be found horizontally, vertically, or diagonally.

```
L  R  E  C  O  R  D  S  N  G  E  S
L  C  U  P  O  T  T  E  R  Y  T  G
T  I  I  S  W  J  E  U  R  O  S  J
Y  C  P  N  F  U  A  S  R  I  C  G
P  A  M  E  S  Y  B  Y  S  H  W  N
B  G  K  T  N  A  T  R  O  P  M  I
S  Q  I  S  P  E  C  I  A  L  L  D
H  S  B  I  L  A  S  M  K  T  X  L
A  Z  L  L  R  Z  B  P  E  Y  D  O
R  L  E  B  Q  E  P  O  D  M  N  M
E  R  X  D  E  H  S  I  L  O  P  R
S  F  G  O  C  L  E  A  N  S  E  D
```

NEW WORDS

polished	storyteller
important	shares
listens	records
molding	cleansed
soaked	pottery

DID YOU KNOW

✻ *Pueblo* is a Spanish word that means "village" or "town."

✻ The Cochiti Pueblo people are also famous for the drums that they make. They create the drums using the wood from large aspen or cottonwood trees and deer or cow hides.

✻ Today the Cochiti people still live in adobe houses just as their ancestors did. They make adobe bricks by mixing clay, straw, and water together. When the bricks dry, they become very strong and also insulate the house from hot and cold weather

FIND OUT MORE–READ:

- "Pueblo Pottery." (*National Geographic*, November, 1992)
- *Arts and Crafts Modeling* by Susie O'Reilly. (Thomson Learning, 1993)
- *Pueblo Storyteller* by Diane Hoyt-Goldsmith. (Holiday House, 1991)

STORYTIME

 Do you know this storyteller? It is President Clinton sharing a story with children at the White House. Imagine that you could tell a story to President Clinton. What would your story be about?

These questions will help guide your writing:

- What is the topic of your story?
- What characters are in your story?
- What happens to the characters in your story?

Use at least four New Words in your paragraph.

 You've read all the stories. Now take the test!

SECRETS TO SUCCESS ON TESTS

Look at all possible answers. Leave out the ones that you know are incorrect. Decide which of the remaining answers is better or best.

Read each phrase. Select the word or phrase that means the same as the underlined word. Fill in the circle for the answer at the bottom of the page.

1 shares his wealth

A	soaks	**C**	confines
B	contributes	**D**	spends

2 molding the clay

A	soaking	**C**	watching
B	sharing	**D**	shaping

3 records of history

A	accounts	**C**	listened
B	important	**D**	times

4 polished the stone

A	soaked	**C**	smoothed
B	shared	**D**	wrote

Read each set of sentences. Select the word that completes the first sentence according to the stated meaning. Fill in the circle for the answer at the bottom of the page.

5 The children gathered in a tight circle around the ____ . Which word indicates a person who passes on the heritage of a people through stories?

A	Cochiti	**C**	storyteller
B	Pueblo	**D**	parents

6 It is ____ that you learn to read good books. Which word indicates that reading good books has a lot of value?

A	soaked	**C**	polished
B	important	**D**	written

7 Our coats were ____ from being out in the storm. Which word indicates that the coats were completely wet?

A	important	**C**	polished
B	soaked	**D**	cleansed

8 My mother ____ to me when I practice. Which word indicates that the speaker's mother hears and pays attention to the practice?

A	listens	**C**	shares
B	records	**D**	watches

9 We ____ the bowl before putting food into it. Which word indicates that the bowl was made clean?

A	shares	**C**	polished
B	soaked	**D**	cleansed

10 Many Pueblos earn their living by making ____ . Which word indicates pots and dishes made from baked clay?

A	polished	**C**	pottery
B	molding	**D**	stone

11 She ____ the cost of the apartment with a friend. Which word indicates that both the speaker and friend pay the cost of the apartment?

A	soaked	**C**	records
B	shares	**D**	cleansed

12 ____ the clay into various shapes takes a lot of skill. Which word indicates that what takes so much skill is the forming or shaping of the clay?

A	Missing	**C**	Molding
B	Mixing	**D**	Managing

ANSWERS

1	Ⓐ Ⓑ Ⓒ Ⓓ	4	Ⓐ Ⓑ Ⓒ Ⓓ	7	Ⓐ Ⓑ Ⓒ Ⓓ	10	Ⓐ Ⓑ Ⓒ Ⓓ
2	Ⓐ Ⓑ Ⓒ Ⓓ	5	Ⓐ Ⓑ Ⓒ Ⓓ	8	Ⓐ Ⓑ Ⓒ Ⓓ	11	Ⓐ Ⓑ Ⓒ Ⓓ
3	Ⓐ Ⓑ Ⓒ Ⓓ	6	Ⓐ Ⓑ Ⓒ Ⓓ	9	Ⓐ Ⓑ Ⓒ Ⓓ	12	Ⓐ Ⓑ Ⓒ Ⓓ

STOP

HOT AIR LIFTS BALLOON!

Pilot Has No Control!
Friends Give Chase!

Below is a magical kingdom. Houses look like gift boxes; roads look like ribbon. You float along in a fairy-tale world. People look up and wave. Your ticket into this land is a hot air balloon!

Ballooning has become a popular sport. Balloonists hold races and **festivals** where they **exchange information** and adventure stories.

Most hot air balloons are bigger than a house. They can float because hot air is lighter than cool air. A wind machine fills the balloon with air which is then heated by a small burner. You can't really **steer** a balloon. A pilot makes it go up or down until the wind pushes it in the right direction. **Passengers** ride in a basket **attached** to the bottom of the balloon. The major **risks** are **tangling** with power lines or treetops and bumpy landings.

A ground **crew** follows the balloon in a chase **vehicle**. When the balloon lands, the crew squeezes out the air and packs it in the vehicle.

The balloonists look forward to the next time they will float up, up, and away!

"Spirits high after balloon safely descends!" says pilot.

Which comes first?
Number these statements 1-4.

- [ ] Air is squeezed out of the balloon.
- [ ] Air in the balloon is heated.
- [ ] The ground crew chases the ba[lloon.]
- [ ] The balloon is filled with ai[r.]

Dictionary Lifts Words to New Heights!

Add the New Words to the alphabetical list below.

_____

attention

crest

_____

_____

inflame

_____

_____

past

_____

steam

_____

_____

wagon

New Words

exchange   risks
crew   attached
vehicle   information
steer   passengers
tangling   festivals

Need help? Check out the glossary on page 103.

Discover The Hidden Meanings

Write a letter on each line to match each New Word with its meaning.

___ 1. attached

___ 2. festivals

___ 3. risks

___ 4. crew

___ 5. vehicle

___ 6. information

___ 7. tangling

___ 8. passengers

___ 9. exchange

___ 10. steer

a. to give in return for something else; trade

b. chances of getting hurt, or of losing; danger

c. days or times of feasting or celebrating; happy holidays

d. facts or knowledge about something

e. fastened or joined together by sticking or tying

f. people traveling in a car, bus, plane, or other vehicle, but not helping to operate it

g. a group of people working together

h. to guide by means of a rudder or wheel; direct the movement of

i. something that carries persons or things over land or in space, such as an automobile or a spacecraft

j. becoming knotted, twisted, or confused

Flying Facts

In 1988, Per Lindstrand of Great Britain reached 65,000 feet in his balloon. That's a record for the highest altitude ever achieved in a balloon.

59

Lost Words Drop Out of Sky!

Write a New Word on each line to finish each sentence.

New Words

risks

exchange

steer

vehicle

information

festivals

passengers

tangling

attached

crew

1. Carol found some _____ on snakes in the encyclopedia.

2. Ben could not _____ his bicycle because his handlebars were loose.

3. Smoking and drinking are major health _____ .

4. Do you want to _____ your dump truck for my tractor?

5. James watched as the road _____ put up new traffic signals.

6. The pilot told the _____ to return to their seats.

7. That _____ looks like it is part car and part truck.

8. We enjoy attending cultural _____ .

9. David _____ some stickers to his bicycle.

10. The wind kept _____ Dad's fishing line.

THE SHOCKING TRUTH ABOUT PREFIXES

☞ A **prefix** is a word part that can be added to the beginning of a root word. The prefix <u>mis</u> means wrong or bad.

prefix		root word		new word
mis	+	take	=	mistake

Look at these root words. Add the prefix <u>mis</u> to the root to make the New Word. Then draw a line from the New Word to its meaning.

Root Word	New Word	Meaning
1. information	_____	a. wrong step
2. judge	_____	b. place wrongly
3. place	_____	c. match badly
4. step	_____	d. wrong information
5. spell	_____	e. use wrongly
6. match	_____	f. bad adventure
7. adventure	_____	g. judge unfairly
8. use	_____	h. spell wrongly
9. treat	_____	i. understand wrongly
10. understand	_____	j. treat badly

CATegories

Circle the three words that fit in each category.

1. [things you can **exchange**]	money	toys	brothers	stories
2. [kinds of <u>vehicles</u>]	house	truck	tractor	plane
3. [things that are easily <u>attached</u>]	string	stickers	metal	tape
4. [what is done at <u>festivals</u>]	singing	dancing	laughing	crying
5. [things you can <u>steer</u>]	bicycle	sled	car	balloon
6. [carries many <u>passengers</u>]	train	bicycle	bus	jet
7. [sources of <u>information</u>]	encyclopedia	newspaper	magazine	balloon

More exciting stories about BALLOONING!

- *Around the World in Eighty Days* by Jules Verne. (Viking Press, 1980)
- *Victorious Paints the Great Balloon* by David Francis Birchman.
  (Bradbury Press, 1991)

Parents Fear Hot Air Balloon Craze!

 In your journal, write a paragraph that will convince your parents to go up in a hot air balloon with you.

As you write, think about questions like these:

- How would it make you feel?
- What would you see?
- What would you always remember?

Use at least four New Words in your paragraph.

Come in out of the rain and take the test!

SCORE HIGHER ON TESTS

Be alert to an answer that is related to the given word but does not mean the same thing.

Read each phrase. Select the word or phrase that means the __same__ as the underlined word. Fill in the circle for the answer at the bottom of the page.

1 to exchange places

   A know
   B find
   C trade
   D tangle

2 unnecessary risks

   A accidents
   B lessons
   C dangers
   D landings

3 the crew worked

   A team
   B men
   C women
   D passengers

4 steer the car

   A wash
   B guide
   C start
   D ride in

5 a red vehicle

   A balloon
   B scarf
   C suit
   D carrier

6 read the information

   A facts
   B encyclopedia
   C newspaper
   D numbers

Complete each definition with the best word or phrase. Fill in the circle for the answer at the bottom of the page.

7 To be attached is to be—

   A exchanged
   B tangled
   C joined
   D separated

8 Passengers are people who—

   A steer a balloon
   B take risks
   C follow a balloon
   D ride in a vehicle

9 To be tangling with something is to be—

   A twisting together
   B putting it in order
   C landing
   D steering

10 Festivals are—

   A risks
   B celebrations
   C vehicles
   D balloons

11 To exchange information is to—

   A use it
   B share it
   C write it
   D draw it

12 A risk is a—

   A sport
   B hot air balloon
   C crew
   D possible danger

ANSWERS

1	Ⓐ Ⓑ Ⓒ Ⓓ	4	Ⓐ Ⓑ Ⓒ Ⓓ	7	Ⓐ Ⓑ Ⓒ Ⓓ	10	Ⓐ Ⓑ Ⓒ Ⓓ
2	Ⓐ Ⓑ Ⓒ Ⓓ	5	Ⓐ Ⓑ Ⓒ Ⓓ	8	Ⓐ Ⓑ Ⓒ Ⓓ	11	Ⓐ Ⓑ Ⓒ Ⓓ
3	Ⓐ Ⓑ Ⓒ Ⓓ	6	Ⓐ Ⓑ Ⓒ Ⓓ	9	Ⓐ Ⓑ Ⓒ Ⓓ	12	Ⓐ Ⓑ Ⓒ Ⓓ

THIS DOG RESCUES HIKERS

Once people traveled by foot across the **steep**, snow-covered Swiss Alps in Europe. Many became lost in storms or froze to death as they slept. An **avalanche** could easily **bury** a person in its path.

Monks who lived in the Alps trained St. Bernards to **rescue** people. These giant dogs were **ideal** for this work. They were large, but gentle and had high **intelligence**. A St. Bernard could **sniff** out people even when they were buried **underneath** the snow.

One of the most famous St. Bernards was Barry. During his twelve years of **duty**, he saved forty people. One story tells of this dog finding a little boy who had fallen asleep on an icy mountain **ledge**. Barry covered the freezing boy with his own body. Then Barry licked the boy's face until he opened his eyes. Barry was able to get the boy to climb on his broad, strong back. As the boy clung to his thick fur, Barry carried him to safety.

Today there is a monument to Barry's heroic rescues. Also, in his memory the best St. Bernards are often called "Barry."

IS THAT A FACT?

Are the following sentences facts or opinions?

Write an F if the sentence is fact or an O if it is opinion.

1. ___ Barry rescued forty people.

2. ___ St. Bernards are the best dogs to have for a pet.

3. ___ People enjoy traveling to the Alps.

4. ___ The Alps are in Switzerland.

ALPHABET AVALANCHE

Write the New Words in alphabetical order.

available

_____

burst

_____

_____

_____

identify

intake

_____

_____

_____

research

snicker

_____

_____

NEW WORDS

bury

underneath

avalanche

sniff

ideal

rescue

duty

intelligence

steep

ledge

 PERFECT MATCH
FOUND BETWEEN WORDS AND MEANINGS

Use context clues or the glossary to match each New Word below with its meaning.

Write the correct letter on the line.

____ 1. ideal

____ 2. sniff

____ 3. avalanche

____ 4. bury

____ 5. steep

____ 6. rescue

____ 7. underneath

____ 8. ledge

____ 9. duty

____ 10. intelligence

a. slanting sharply up or down; having a sharp slope

b. things that are done as a part of a person's work; what is required

c. exactly as one would wish; perfect

d. to free from danger or evil

e. to take in short breaths through the nose as when trying to smell something

f. a flat part like a narrow shelf that comes out from a cliff or wall

g. a large mass of snow, ice, or rocks sliding swiftly down a mountain

h. the ability to learn and understand, or to solve problems

i. under; below; beneath

j. to cover up so as to hide

MISSING WORDS RESCUED
NOW THEY'RE FINISHING THEIR SENTENCES

Finish these sentences. Write a New Word on each line.

I watched the squirrel as it scurried down the _____ hill. It would often

stop and _____ the ground. I wondered, "Did that squirrel _____

nuts, or did it just want a bite of my sandwich?" I finished eating and decided the day

was _____ for hiking. Soon my squirrel friend jumped out at me from

_____ a bush. It seemed to want me to follow. I did my _____

and followed it through the snow. There on a high _____ was a baby squirrel.

If I could not find a way to _____ it, the baby squirrel might be killed in an

_____ . I found a long tree branch and led the baby to safety. Because of the

_____ of the mother, soon both were chattering thanks to me.

LEARN TO SPOT WORDS WITH MULTIPLE MEANINGS

👉 Many words have more than one meaning. **Context clues** will tell you which meaning a
word has in a sentence. Each word below is used in two different ways.

Read each sentence. Find the meaning of each underlined word. Write the correct number on the line.

bury

1. to put a dead body in a grave

2. to hide or cover up

ledge

1. a flat surface coming out from the
   side of a mountain

2. a narrow shelf that sticks out from a wall

duty

1. part of a person's work

2. a tax paid on goods brought into the country

_____ 1. Betty <u>buried</u> her face in her hands.

_____ 2. I will <u>bury</u> the bird in our garden.

_____ 3. Mrs. Torres put a potted plant on
   the window <u>ledge</u>.

_____ 4. Ben lowered a rope to the <u>ledge</u> and
   climbed down quickly.

_____ 5. Jason's <u>duties</u> include feeding the
   dog and taking out the garbage.

_____ 6. The ship's captain paid the <u>duty</u> to
   the officers.

ARE PICTURES WORTH A THOUSAND WORDS?

Write a New Word to tell what each picture shows.

NEW WORDS

bury

sniff

ledge

underneath

avalanche

rescue

1. _____

2. _____

3. _____

4. _____

5. _____

6. _____

SNOW JOB
PORTRAIT OF A ST. BERNARD IN ACTION

Write a story about the rescue taking place in the picture. Share your story with a friend.

These questions will help guide your writing:

• Where was this man?

• How did the dogs help him?

• What do you think will happen when they get back?

Use at least four New Words in your story.

DOGGIE TIDBITS

🦴 Dogs can only sweat through their tongues and the bottoms of their paws. That's why they stick their tongues out on hot summer days.

🦴 All dogs have a natural urge to sing. In the wild, they will gather to howl or bay at the moon. As pets, they will respond to certain musical tones or instruments.

READ MORE ABOUT IT

• *Judge Benjamin, The Superdog Surprise* by Judith McInerney. (Holiday House, 1985)

• *Big Ben* by David Harry Walker. (Houghton Mifflin, 1969)

• *A Dog and a Half* by Barbara Willard. (T. Nelson, 1971)

• *Understanding Man's Best Friend* by Ann Squire. (Macmillan, 1991)

• *Dogs: The Wolf Within* by Dorothy Hinsha Patent. (Carolrhoda, 1993)

Stay on the trail for the test!

SECRETS TO SUCCESS ON TESTS

Answer all test questions of which you are sure. After you have gone through the test once, go back to the difficult questions.

Read each sentence. Select the word that best completes each one. Fill in the circle for the answer at the bottom of the page.

1 The _____ stairs were hard to climb.

   A underneath
   B steep
   C ideal
   D short

2 Our dog likes to _____ its bones in the garden.

   A find
   B lose
   C bury
   D dig

3 The firefighter will _____ the people from the burning building.

   A rescue
   B watch
   C return
   D research

4 Tom is the _____ person to do that job.

   A idol
   B idle
   C idea
   D ideal

5 Your parents have a _____ to take care of you.

   A ideal
   B duty
   C rescue
   D avalanche

6 The dog was stuck on a rocky _____.

   A avalanche
   B rescue
   C ledge
   D storm

Read the paragraphs. Select the words that best fit in the blanks. Fill in the circles for the answers at the bottom of the page.

Saint Bernards have more __7__ than most dogs. They have been trained to __8__ out people who may have lost their way in the snow. Many people have these dogs to thank for rescue from such dangers as an __9__.

We had been climbing the __10__ mountain all day, so we looked for a place to camp for the night. To our surprise we found the __11__ spot to pitch our tent and slept comfortably __12__ our warm blankets.

7 **A** ideal   **C** duty
     B intelligence   **D** shine

8 **A** find   **C** sniff
     B point   **D** carry

9 **A** area   **C** automobile
     B avalanche   **D** auction

10 **A** flat   **C** underneath
      B ideal   **D** steep

11 **A** underneath   **C** idea
      B ideal   **D** idol

12 **A** beside   **C** steep
      B underneath   **D** ledge

ANSWERS

1 Ⓐ Ⓑ Ⓒ Ⓓ	4 Ⓐ Ⓑ Ⓒ Ⓓ	7 Ⓐ Ⓑ Ⓒ Ⓓ	10 Ⓐ Ⓑ Ⓒ Ⓓ
2 Ⓐ Ⓑ Ⓒ Ⓓ	5 Ⓐ Ⓑ Ⓒ Ⓓ	8 Ⓐ Ⓑ Ⓒ Ⓓ	11 Ⓐ Ⓑ Ⓒ Ⓓ
3 Ⓐ Ⓑ Ⓒ Ⓓ	6 Ⓐ Ⓑ Ⓒ Ⓓ	9 Ⓐ Ⓑ Ⓒ Ⓓ	12 Ⓐ Ⓑ Ⓒ Ⓓ

AND THE WINNER IS... MAYA LIN

T he winner of one of the most important design **competitions** ever held was not a **famous** artist or **architect**. It was a twenty-one-year-old Yale student. Maya Ying Lin, a Chinese American from Ohio, was chosen from among 1,421 artists to design the Vietnam Veterans Memorial in Washington, D.C.

The **memorial** she designed honors the United States men and women who served in the Vietnam War (1959-1975). On the five-hundred-foot, shiny, black granite, V-shaped wall are **chiseled** the names of the more than 58,156 people who gave their lives or are missing in action.

"The Wall" was opened on Veterans Day, November 13, 1982. Visitors touch, **trace**, and even kiss the names. **Medals**, letters, and children's photos are often left at the wall.

The memorial made young Maya Lin famous. Today she runs an architectural **studio** in New York. She designs houses, **sculptures**, and

other memorials. In 1991, Maya Lin designed a living sculpture of ramps and shrubs cut to look like a pinball machine. It stands outside a North Carolina sports **arena**, waiting for a giant who likes to play pinball!

GIVE ME THE FACTS

Are the following statements fact or opinion?
Write an F is the sentence is a fact; write an O if it is an opinion.

_____ 1. "The Wall" is the most touching memorial in Washington, D.C.

_____ 2. As a student at Yale University, Maya Lin was chosen to design the Vietnam Veterans Memorial.

_____ 3. Maya Lin is a very creative architect.

_____ 4. Maya Lin runs an architectural studio in New York.

GIVE THESE WORDS SOME ORDER, PLEASE!

New Words

competitions

famous

architect

memorial

chiseled

trace

medals

studio

sculptures

arena

👉 In the dictionary, **guide words** at the top of the page mark the first and last entry on the page.

Write the New Words between the correct guide words.

apple/chute

_____

_____

_____

coin/farmer

_____

_____

mechanic/memory

_____

_____

sail/track

_____

_____

MEANINGS REVEALED

👉 **Context clues** are words in a sentence or phrase that help you understand the meaning of a word. Look for context clues to help you match each New Word with its meaning.

Write the correct letter on each line.

_____ 1. trace

_____ 2. memorial

_____ 3. famous

_____ 4. medals

_____ 5. studio

_____ 6. sculptures

_____ 7. chiseled

_____ 8. arena

_____ 9. architect

_____ 10. competitions

a. objects, often flat pieces of metal, awarded for achievement

b. person who designs buildings and other structures

c. a stadium or amphitheater; a place where public events are held

d. carved, cut, and designed objects

e. contests

f. shaped or carved with a chisel

g. the workplace of an artist or a designer

h. well-known

i. a structure built to remember a person or group of people

j. to draw an outline

MISSING WORDS FOUND

Use New Words to complete these sentences.

1. Michael ran back to the _____ to get the drawings he had left on his desk.

2. He had to mail them by 5:00 P.M. to be entered in the upcoming _____ .

3. The _____ and engineer have worked together for many years.

4. Next summer they will be constructing their dream project, the city's sports _____ .

5. Michelangelo, the _____ artist and architect, lived in Italy.

6. The "Pieta" is one of his most famous _____ .

7. An award on which my name is _____ hangs on my window.

8. Terry, my youngest daughter, likes to _____ the ornament with paper and pencil.

9. Uncle Jim keeps the _____ he earned from the Vietnam War on his bookshelf.

10. He will wear his uniform when he goes to the _____ in Washington, D.C.

WORKING WITH SYL -LA- BLES

☞ Words can be divided into smaller word parts or **syllables**. Say each word below and listen for the syllables.

pop u lar   di ges tion

Write each word leaving a space between syllables.

1. memorial _____

2. famous _____

3. medals _____

4. studio _____

5. sculptures _____

6. chiseled _____

7. arena _____

8. architect _____

9. competitions _____

10. convention _____

IT'S IN THE GENES
Since both of her parents were artists, Maya Lin did not want to become one. She liked biology and planned to major in zoology. Instead, she ended up getting a degree in architecture!

DID IT MAKE THE GRADE?
Designing the Vietnam Veterans Memorial was a class assignment for Maya Lin. She got a B from her teacher!

70

BETWEEN ONE THING AND ANOTHER

👉 **Analogies** show the relationship between things.

toothbrush is to **teeth** as **brush** is to **hair**

Use a New Word to complete each analogy.

1. carved is to wood as _____ is to stone

2. artist is to _____ as family is to house

3. theater is to plays as _____ is to sports

4. _____ are to sculptors as books are to writers

5. _____ are to athletes as conventions are to businesspeople

6. unknown is to _____ as war is to peace

7. _____ is to pencil as sew is to needle

8. _____ are to heroes as trophies are to athletes

New Words

competitions

famous

architect

memorial

chiseled

trace

medals

studio

sculptures

arena

THE ART OF BEING AN ARTIST

Would you like to be a famous artist? Write a paragraph describing what you might do to accomplish your goal.

These questions will help guide your writing:

- What kind of artist would you like to be?

- What types of skills are necessary?

- What type of training would you need?

Use at least four New Words in your writing.

READ MORE ABOUT IT

- *Maya Lin* by Lynn Yokoe. (Modern Curriculum Press, 1995)

- *The Story of the Vietnam Veterans Memorial* by David K. Wright. (Childrens Press, 1989)

- *The Wall* by Eve Bunting. (Clarion Books, 1990)

- *A Wall of Names* by Judy Donnelly. (Random House, 1991)

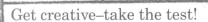
Get creative–take the test!

71

TEST-TAKING SECRETS REVEALED

If you make a mistake, erase the incorrect answer entirely. Don't forget to mark the correct answer for that question.

Read each group of words. Select the word or words that mean the same as the underlined word. Fill in the circle for the answer at the bottom of the page.

1 chiseled the stone

  A cut   **C** traced
  B polished   **D** weighed

2 a famous person

  A good   **C** skilled
  B well-known   **D** funny

3 wore medals

  A rocks
  B stones
  C small objects given as awards
  D small objects used for coins

4 decorated with sculptures

  A paintings   **C** statues
  B buildings   **D** walls

5 played in the arena

  A school   **C** apartment
  B house   **D** stadium

6 a memorial in Washington

  A school
  B sign
  C reminder of an event or person
  D award for good service

Read each set of sentences. Select the word or words that best complete the second sentence in each set. Fill in the circle for the answer at the bottom of the page.

7 I entered all the competitions I could but did not win any of them.
Competitions means—

  A contests   **C** games
  B stores   **D** sports

8 The architect planned the building to rise out of the water.
An architect is a—

  A artist   **C** designer
  B worker   **D** painter

9 The artist created a memorial.
Memorial means—

  A wall   **C** museum
  B painting   **D** remembrance

10 He was a famous football player
Famous means—

  A funny   **C** well-liked
  B well-known   **D** older

11 Use this stencil to trace your name.
Trace means to—

  A outline   **C** write
  B cut   **D** paint

12 The natural light in the studio helps the artist in choosing colors. Studio means—

  A closet
  B place where an artist works
  C place where people study
  D porch

ANSWERS							
1 Ⓐ Ⓑ Ⓒ Ⓓ	4 Ⓐ Ⓑ Ⓒ Ⓓ	7 Ⓐ Ⓑ Ⓒ Ⓓ	10 Ⓐ Ⓑ Ⓒ Ⓓ
2 Ⓐ Ⓑ Ⓒ Ⓓ	5 Ⓐ Ⓑ Ⓒ Ⓓ	8 Ⓐ Ⓑ Ⓒ Ⓓ	11 Ⓐ Ⓑ Ⓒ Ⓓ
3 Ⓐ Ⓑ Ⓒ Ⓓ	6 Ⓐ Ⓑ Ⓒ Ⓓ	9 Ⓐ Ⓑ Ⓒ Ⓓ	12 Ⓐ Ⓑ Ⓒ Ⓓ

NOLAN RYAN — STRIKE-OUT KING

Nolan Ryan did not **aspire** to be a professional baseball player. Although a **gifted** high school athlete, he set out to be a veterinarian. But because of his **undeniable** talent for baseball, he was **coaxed** into signing a contract with the New York Mets upon his graduation.

Although **acclaimed** for his fastball, Ryan lacked **consistency** and control. After enjoying only **sporadic** success, Nolan was traded to the California Angels in 1971. He led the league in strike-outs. A year later, he tied the record for "no-hitters."

Nolan Ryan's famous fastball, once clocked at 100.9 MPH, enabled him to join the Houston Astros in 1979. He soon became the all-time major league strike-out leader. Ryan's **illustrious** career continued in 1989 with the Texas Rangers. When the "Strike-out King" retired in 1993, his **achievements** included over 5,500 strike-outs and seven "no hitters."

However, Nolan Ryan never received the **coveted** Cy Young Award. But that didn't seem to bother him. He simply wanted to be remembered as "a guy who just went out each time and did his best."

PUT THE STORY IN ORDER

What happened first?

Number these events 1 to 4.

_____ The Strike-out King retires.

_____ Ryan ties the record for "no-hitters."

_____ Ryan joins Texas Rangers.

_____ Ryan pitches for the Mets.

THE AMAZING ALPHABET

☞ In the dictionary, **guide words** at the top of the page mark the first and last entry on that page.

Write the New Words between the correct guide words below.

able/attitude

_____

_____

_____

catch/deny

_____

_____

_____

gall/import

_____

_____

soccer/union

_____

_____

Need help?
Use the
dictionary.

New Words

coveted	undeniable	achievements
aspire	coaxed	sporadic
gifted	acclaimed	illustrious
	consistency	

MEANINGS BROUGHT TO LIGHT!

Use context clues to match each New Word with its meaning. Write the correct letter on each line.

____ 1. illustrious

____ 2. coveted

____ 3. sporadic

____ 4. achievements

____ 5. undeniable

____ 6. acclaimed

____ 7. coaxed

____ 8. consistency

____ 9. gifted

____ 10. aspire

a. to desire to achieve a goal

b. uneven or inconsistent

c. persuaded by praise or promises

d. having special talents or skills

e. outstanding; characterized by greatness

f. greatly wanted or desired

g. without dispute or disagreement

h. given high praise

i. goals reached or accomplished

j. conformity over time; evenness

MISSING WORD ALERT

Use New Words to complete these sentences.

1. My teenage cousins _____ to be all-around athletes.

2. Their grandfather has told them stories about the _____ career of Babe Ruth.

3. By the age of five, the girl was an obviously _____ pianist.

4. Though her talents were _____ , she still had to practice for many hours.

5. The _____ author has received awards for his work from all around the world.

6. Of all his _____ , however, he treasures his Pulitzer Prize the most.

7. The swimming instructor _____ the boy to jump into the water.

8. The instructor had won a _____ Olympic gold medal.

9. When Carla first started learning the high jump, her ability to get over the bar was _____ .

10. With practice and training from her coach, her _____ increased.

New Words
coveted
aspire
gifted
undeniable
coaxed
acclaimed
consistency
sporadic
illustrious
achievements

WORKING WITH SYNONYMS AND ANTONYMS

Synonyms are words with nearly the same meaning. **Antonyms** are words that have opposite meanings.

Begin and **start** are synonyms.

Under and **over** are antonyms.

Word List

usual	win	begin	irregular	enemy	fail
support	pal	power	finish	weakness	discourage

Use words from the word list to fill in the blanks.

	SYNONYM	WORD		ANTONYM
1.	_____	strength		_____
2.	_____	encourage		_____
3.	_____	regular		_____
4.	_____	friend		_____
5.	_____	lose		_____
6.	_____	start		_____

SOLVE THIS PUZZLE

Use New Words to finish the crossword puzzle.

New Words

coveted	undeniable	consistency	illustrious	coaxed
achievements	acclaimed	sporadic	aspire	gifted

Across

1. the _____ truth
4. uneven
6. an _____ career
7. talented
8. accomplishments
9. persuaded
10. greatly desired

Down

2. _____ to greatness
3. highly praised
5. evenness

BASEBALL BULLETS

 Nolan Ryan officially retired from baseball at the age of 46.

 Did you know that Nolan Ryan's 1968 rookie baseball card is reportedly worth up to $1,700?

FIND OUT MORE ABOUT NOLAN RYAN AND BASEBALL

READ THESE BOOKS:

- *Baseball's Finest Pitchers* by Nathan Aaseng. (Lerner Publications, 1980)

- *Sports Heroes: Great Pitchers* by P.R. Emert. (GRA Publishing Group, 1990)

THE THRILL OF VICTORY, THE AGONY OF DEFEAT

Think of a team that you are on or one that you would like to be on. Have you ever dreamed about winning the big game for your team? Write a story with a friend about what it would be like to be the winner or loser of a big game.

These questions will help guide your writing:

- What did you do?
- How did your teammates react?
- How did you feel?

Use at least four New Words in your story.

Bat your way to the test!

TEST-DAY TIPS TOLD

If you have time at the end of a test, reread the directions and test questions.

Read each group of words. Select the word or words that mean the opposite of the underlined word. Fill in the circle for the answer at the bottom of the page.

1 <u>illustrious</u> scientist

    A successful   **C** unknown

    B very famous   **D** very smart

2 <u>sporadic</u> efforts

    A strong

    B from time to time

    C from one to the other

    D regular

3 proud of his <u>achievements</u>

    A successes   **C** events

    B failures   **D** looks

4 <u>undeniable</u> truth

    A believed   **C** true

    B taught   **D** disputable

5 treated with <u>consistency</u>

    A an expected way

    B always the same way

    C never the same way

    D with great care

6 <u>acclaimed</u> for her work

    A blamed   **C** chosen

    B praised   **D** hired

Read each set of sentences. Select the word that completes the first sentence according to the stated meaning. Fill in the circle for the answer at the bottom of the page.

7 The ____ scientist made several great discoveries. Which word indicates that the scientist has great natural ability?

    A illustrious   **C** gifted

    B undeniable   **D** sporadic

8 The athlete won the ____ award. Which word indicates the award is highly desired?

    A achievement   **C** gifted

    B undeniable   **D** coveted

9 I ____ to be an astronaut. Which word indicates the speaker has a strong desire to be an astronaut?

    A ask   **C** assign

    B aspire   **D** assist

10 He ____ me into going with him. Which word indicates that he kept asking me over and over?

    A acclaimed   **C** coaxed

    B gifted   **D** coveted

11 Sam had only ____ success in growing orchids. Which word indicates that Sam's successes happened once in awhile?

    A sporadic   **C** undeniable

    B illustrious   **D** acclaimed

12 Nolan Ryan has been ____ as one of the greatest pitchers in baseball. Which word indicates that Ryan has been applauded for his skills?

    A acclaimed   **C** coaxed

    B gifted   **D** sporadic

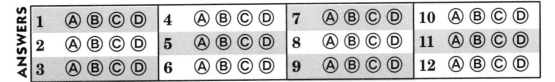

ANSWERS

1	Ⓐ Ⓑ Ⓒ Ⓓ	4	Ⓐ Ⓑ Ⓒ Ⓓ	7	Ⓐ Ⓑ Ⓒ Ⓓ	10	Ⓐ Ⓑ Ⓒ Ⓓ
2	Ⓐ Ⓑ Ⓒ Ⓓ	5	Ⓐ Ⓑ Ⓒ Ⓓ	8	Ⓐ Ⓑ Ⓒ Ⓓ	11	Ⓐ Ⓑ Ⓒ Ⓓ
3	Ⓐ Ⓑ Ⓒ Ⓓ	6	Ⓐ Ⓑ Ⓒ Ⓓ	9	Ⓐ Ⓑ Ⓒ Ⓓ	12	Ⓐ Ⓑ Ⓒ Ⓓ

DEEP FREEZE DOWN UNDER

Brrrr! Imagine a place that is freezing every day, even in the middle of summer. Think of a land where the sun doesn't come up at all in the winter. This place is Antarctica, our earth's South Pole.

In some parts of this frozen land, the **glaciers** are three miles deep. Icebergs bigger than ships float in the ocean. The coldest **temperature** on earth was **recorded** there. It reached 126 **degrees** below zero! Usually, it is too cold to snow. Snow already on the ground blows in the strong winds, making mountains and **plains** of ice. A few animals like penguins, seals, and walruses can live in that cold. They stay near the ocean for warmth and food. There they find fish and seaweed to eat.

What about people? Only **scientists** live there. They build special **shelters** in which to do their **research**.

Can you believe that Antarctica was once a hot, thick jungle? Rocks show that **tropical** plants and animals used to live on its **surface**. You can be sure that there are no jungles there now!

WHAT'S YOUR OPINION?

Which of these statements is a fact, and which is an opinion?

Write an F̲ if the sentence is a fact; write an O̲ if it is an opinion.

____ 1. Glaciers are large masses of ice.

____ 2. Scientists do not like working in Antarctica.

____ 3. Antarctica has the coldest temperatures in the world.

____ 4. The most beautiful animals live in Antarctica.

NO SWEAT WITH THE ALPHABET!

👉 In the dictionary, **guide words** at the top of the page show the first and last entries on the page. All other entries on the page are in alphabetical order between those words.

Write the New Words in alphabetical order under the correct guide words.

definition/pizza

_____

_____

schwa/television

_____

_____

_____

place/school

_____

_____

_____

tell/trouble

_____

_____

New Words

scientists   surface   temperature   degrees   shelters

plains   recorded   glaciers   research   tropical

WORDS AND MEANINGS TOGETHER AGAIN

Match each New Word below with its meaning. Write the letter of the meaning on the line next to the word.

____ 1. tropical

____ 2. temperature

____ 3. research

____ 4. glaciers

____ 5. scientists

____ 6. recorded

____ 7. surface

____ 8. plains

____ 9. shelters

____ 10. degrees

a. experts in science, such as a chemists or biologists

b. written down for future use; kept account of

c. units used in measuring temperature that are shown by the symbol °

d. careful study to find out facts and principles about a subject

e. places or things that cover or protect, as from the weather or danger

f. from the region of the earth that is noted for its hot climate

g. large masses of ice and snow that move very slowly down a mountain or across land until they melt

h. the degree of hotness or coldness, usually measured by a thermometer

i. the outside or outer facing of a thing

j. large stretches of flat land

LOST WORDS RETURN TO SENTENCES

Write the New Words that best complete the sentences.

1. The top _____ of the stove was very hot.

2. When it rained, the boys ran for the _____ .

3. Mr. Johnson _____ our scores in his grade book.

4. At 32 _____ Fahrenheit, water turns to ice.

5. Green plants grow well in the hot, humid climate of a _____ rain forest.

6. Mother took my _____ because she thought I had a fever.

7. Juan went to the library to do some _____ for a report he is writing.

8. Rivers form as the _____ on a mountain begin to melt.

9. Three _____ were given prizes for their discoveries.

10. The soil on the _____ makes good farmland.

New Words

research
glaciers
scientists
shelters
surface
plains
recorded
tropical
temperature
degrees

CONFUSION TAKEN OUT OF MULTIPLE MEANINGS

☞ Many words have more than one meaning. Try looking for **context clues** in the sentence to find the meaning of a word.

Drill can mean <u>a tool with a sharp point</u> or <u>to practice over and over</u>.

Read each pair of sentences. Then write the letter of the correct meaning for each sentence.

____ 1. John bought a new <u>record</u> with his allowance.   a. write down

____ 2. Did you <u>record</u> today's temperature on the chart?   b. a disc with sound

____ 3. Steve will <u>bow</u> to his partner and continue to dance. a. to bend the body

____ 4. That <u>bow</u> looks pretty in your hair.   b. a knot tied with loops

____ 5. Sarah has been <u>present</u> all week.   a. to give

____ 6. The principal will <u>present</u> the award to you.   b. here

____ 7. Remember to <u>wind</u> your watch.   a. turn to tighten

____ 8. A tree blew down in the <u>wind</u> storm.   b. moving air

SOLVE THIS SCRAMBLED WORD PUZZLE

Unscramble the New Words listed below.

1. cfusacr _____

2. tehsrles _____

3. ietscntiss _____

4. pcrlatoi _____

5. rmeapturete _____

6. egderse _____

7. crsgaile _____

8. lnaspi _____

9. dreocder _____

10. screhear _____

Brave Explorer Sends Letter From Strange New Land

Imagine that you have just arrived in a new country. Write a letter to your parents describing what you see and do.

The following questions will help guide you in writing your letter.

- What kind of clothes do you need to wear?
- How do the people live?
- What do you do for fun?

Use at least four New Words in your sentences.

MELTDOWN SPELLS DISASTER!

If the ice sheet that covers most of Antarctica melted, it would raise the sea level all over the world by two hundred feet.

Don't be left out in the cold! Take the test!

CONTINENT QUIZ

Antarctica is the southernmost continent and the fifth largest of the seven continents. Can you name the smallest?

Answer: Australia

BE THE FIRST TO KNOW THE COLD HARD FACTS WITH THESE BOOKS

- *Let's Go To Antarctica* by Keith Lye. (Watts, 1984)

- *Antarctica: Our Last Unspoiled Continent* by Laurence Pringle. (Simon & Schuster, 1992)

- *Let's Visit Antarctica* by Ronald Seth. (Burke, 1983)

IMPROVE YOUR SCORE

When you are asked to fill in a blank in a sentence, read the entire sentence first. Then try each of the possible answers to see which one is best.

Read each sentence. Select the word that best completes the sentence. Fill in the circle for the answer at the bottom of the page.

1 The scientists did their _____ while spending the winter in Antarctica.

A glaciers
B shelters
C research
D plains

2 _____ weather is hot and moist.

A Recorded
B Surface
C Temperature
D Tropical

3 The huge _____ move slowly down the mountain.

A glaciers
B shelters
C plains
D degrees

4 I was cold because the _____ stayed around zero all week.

A degrees
B shelters
C plains
D temperature

5 Tents were the only _____ we had against the rain.

A scientists
B shelters
C research
D surface

6 The average temperature is five _____ higher than it was at this time last month.

A degrees
B shelters
C glaciers
D scientists

Read each set of sentences. Select the answer that best completes the second sentence in the set. Fill in the circle for the answer at the bottom of the page.

7 The scientists worked hard and long on their research. Scientists are women and men who—

A grow food
B build buildings
C work in science
D grow flowers

8 The coach recorded the names of all who wanted to play on the team. Recorded means—

A added
B wrote
C read
D said

9 The battle was fought on the plains outside the city. Plains means—

A hills and valleys
B mountains
C forests
D level and treeless areas

10 The surface of Antarctica is mostly all snow and ice. Surface means—

A underneath
B outer part
C temperatures
D degrees

11 The doctor took my temperature every time I came to see her. Temperature means—

A the number of answers
B the amount of slant
C the level of heat
D the degree of pain

12 Glaciers become icebergs when they break off into the ocean. Glaciers means—

A ships
B masses of ice and snow
C deserts
D masses of earth and rock

ANSWERS

1	Ⓐ Ⓑ Ⓒ Ⓓ	4	Ⓐ Ⓑ Ⓒ Ⓓ	7	Ⓐ Ⓑ Ⓒ Ⓓ	10	Ⓐ Ⓑ Ⓒ Ⓓ
2	Ⓐ Ⓑ Ⓒ Ⓓ	5	Ⓐ Ⓑ Ⓒ Ⓓ	8	Ⓐ Ⓑ Ⓒ Ⓓ	11	Ⓐ Ⓑ Ⓒ Ⓓ
3	Ⓐ Ⓑ Ⓒ Ⓓ	6	Ⓐ Ⓑ Ⓒ Ⓓ	9	Ⓐ Ⓑ Ⓒ Ⓓ	12	Ⓐ Ⓑ Ⓒ Ⓓ

HANG IN AT ZERO G!
CAMPERS SPIN HEAD OVER HEELS

Juan's heart pounds as his vehicle **catapults** out of control. He grips the controls, trying to stop the **circular** motion of his capsule. Will he get back on **course**?

Nearby, Amanda feels the sensation of walking on the moon. Tanya braces herself as the Helix Catapult sends her zooming through time and space to the **gaseous** giant, Jupiter.

Are Juan, Amanda, and Tanya **astronauts**? No, they're student **campers** reaching for the stars at Space Camp. The campers enjoy math and science while learning more about the space program.

Juan is in the Multi-Axis Training **Simulator**. Amanda is bouncing around in the Microgravity Training Chair, and Tanya is experiencing Journey to Jupiter. Others are working at the Zero G Wall. Actually, there's no such thing as **zero gravity**. Still, the training wall is called "Zero G"

because it gives campers the feeling of being **weightless**.

Campers can attend Space Camp at the U.S. Space and Rocket Center in Huntsville, Alabama, or at Space Camp Florida in Titusville, Florida. Why not send for information about these out-of-this-world camps today?

WHAT'S YOUR CONCLUSION?

What is the Zero G Wall?
Check the best answer.

○ a weight-training program for children aspiring to be part of the U.S. Space Program

○ a game in which campers travel to Jupiter

○ a training wall that gives visitors the feeling of weightlessness

○ a U.S. rocket

ALPHABET PUTS WORDS IN ORDER

☞ In the dictionary, **guide words** at the top of the page mark the first and last entry on that page.
Write the New Words between the correct guide words.

academic/church

_____

_____

_____

churn/heavy

_____

_____

_____

mental/still

_____

wallet/zinc

_____

_____

New Words

catapults   campers

course   weightless

circular   gravity

gaseous   simulator

astronauts   zero

MEANINGS FOUND AFTER LONG SEARCH

☞ **Context clues** are words in a sentence or phrase that help you understand the meaning of a word. Look for context clues to help you match each New Word with its meaning.

Write the correct letter on each line.

____ 1. zero

____ 2. simulator

____ 3. circular

____ 4. campers

____ 5. astronauts

____ 6. gravity

____ 7. catapults

____ 8. weightless

____ 9. gaseous

____ 10. course

a. force that pulls things toward the center of Earth

b. a route or direction of movement

c. people who vacation at a camp, often in forested or undeveloped areas

d. without the pull of gravity

e. nothing; the base point number

f. throws or launches an object

g. in a circle

h. made of, or like, gas

i. people who travel in outer space

j. a machine that approximates the conditions found in a particular situation

INVESTIGATE THE HOLES IN THESE STORIES

Use New Words to complete these sentences.

1. The satellite traveled a _____ course around the solar system.

2. Its mission was to determine areas where _____ could travel using current technology.

3. After spending their day rafting down the Cheat River, the _____ were exhausted.

4. Hikers smelled some _____ fumes.

5. Jay was very disappointed when he received _____ points on his driving test.

6. The instructor gave Jay some additional lessons on the electronic _____ before he went on the road again.

7. Neil Armstrong was the first man to feel the moon's weak force of _____ .

8. Much of the country saw how _____ he and the rest of the Apollo crew were in space.

9. The rocket _____ the satellite into space.

10. Nothing can stop the stone as it travels along its _____ .

TAKE OFF FOR NEW ADVENTURES!

READ:

- *Astronaut Training* by Ann Armbruster and Elizabeth A. Taylor. (Watts, 1990)

- *Space Camp* by B.B. Hiller and Neil W. Hiller. (Scholastic, 1986)

- *Space Explorers* by Gregory Vogt. (Watts, 1990)

New Words

- catapults
- course
- circular
- gaseous
- astronauts
- campers
- weightless
- gravity
- simulator
- zero

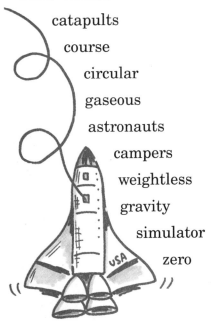

NEW ENDINGS . . .

☞ A **suffix** is a word part that can be added to the end of a root word. Adding a suffix changes the meaning of the word.

Ward means <u>in the direction of</u> or <u>toward</u>.

Add the suffix <u>ward</u> to each underlined root word. Write the new word next to the definition.

DEFINITION	NEW WORD
1. toward the <u>back</u>	_____
2. toward the <u>south</u>	_____
3. toward the <u>east</u>	_____
4. toward the <u>sea</u>	_____
5. toward the <u>north</u>	_____
6. toward the <u>west</u>	_____

ANALOGIES HAVE MEANINGFUL RELATIONSHIPS

👉 **Analogies** show us the relationships between things.

shampoo is to **hair** as **soap** is to **skin**

Use a word from the word list to finish each analogy.

1. _____ is to <u>launches</u> as <u>catches</u> is to <u>captures</u>

2. <u>upward</u> is to <u>downward</u> as <u>forward</u> is to _____

3. <u>divers</u> are to <u>ocean</u> as _____ are to <u>outer</u> space

4. <u>angry</u> is to _____ as <u>happy</u> is to <u>laugh</u>

5. <u>bird</u> is to _____ as <u>bee</u> is to <u>hive</u>

6. _____ is to <u>hot</u> as <u>refrigerator</u> is to <u>cold</u>

7. <u>inhale</u> is to <u>exhale</u> as _____ is to <u>exclude</u>

8. _____ is to <u>circle</u> as <u>straight</u> is to <u>line</u>

9. _____ is to <u>road</u> as <u>height</u> is to <u>building</u>

10. <u>hear</u> is to <u>ears</u> as <u>sight</u> is to _____

WORD LIST

oven

snarl

catapults

nest

length

curved

eyes

backward

astronauts

include

OUT-OF-THIS-WORLD FACTS

✳ You can contact Space Camp at 1-800-63 SPACE or at Post Office Box 070015, Huntsville, Alabama 35807-7015.

✳ You can see the only full-scale model of the Hubble Space Telescope at the U.S. Space and Rocket Center in Huntsville, Alabama.

✳ In the Centrifuge at Space Camp, forty-six people at a time can experience the multi "G" forces of launch and re-entry.

SPACED OUT!

📔 Imagine that you are traveling through outer space. Write a story with a friend describing what you see. Share your story with the class.

These questions will help guide your writing:

• What can you see from your spacecraft?

• How long have you been traveling?

• Do you think that there is life on other planets?

Use at least four New Words in your story.

Catapult into the test!

SECRETS TO SUCCESS ON TESTS

Go back to the story to see how the key word is used there. This will help you to see its meaning.

Read each group of words. Select the word or words that mean the __same__ as the underlined word. Fill in the circle for the answer at the bottom of the page.

1   <u>campers</u> in the tent

   A   lights   **C**   stakes
   B   containers   **D**   vacationers

2   <u>weightless</u> condition

   A   sick
   B   having no weight
   C   tired
   D   having a weight problem

3   <u>astronauts</u> in space

   A   trained space travelers
   B   athletes
   C   outdoor vacationers
   D   teachers

4   <u>gaseous</u> matter

   A   liquid   **C**   natural gas
   B   solid   **D**   in the form of gas

5   force of <u>gravity</u>

   A   push away from earth
   B   pull toward earth
   C   wind power
   D   electric power

6   stay on <u>course</u>

   A   running
   B   working
   C   a way of acting
   D   a particular direction

Complete each definition with the best word. Fill in the circle for the answer at the bottom of the page.

7   A training device that creates situations is a . . . .

   A   simulator
   B   gravity
   C   catapult
   D   course

8   A word that means launches is . . . .

   A   simulators
   B   gravity
   C   catapults
   D   course

9   Something that is round is . . . .

   A   weightless
   B   circular
   C   gaseous
   D   zooming

10   A word that means none or nothing is . . . .

   A   weightless
   B   gravity
   C   circular
   D   zero

11   A pulling force in the earth is . . . .

   A   course
   B   gravity
   C   stone
   D   gaseous

12   To be going in the right direction is to be going on . . . .

   A   course
   B   weightless
   C   circular
   D   zero

ANSWERS

1 Ⓐ Ⓑ Ⓒ Ⓓ	4 Ⓐ Ⓑ Ⓒ Ⓓ	7 Ⓐ Ⓑ Ⓒ Ⓓ	10 Ⓐ Ⓑ Ⓒ Ⓓ
2 Ⓐ Ⓑ Ⓒ Ⓓ	5 Ⓐ Ⓑ Ⓒ Ⓓ	8 Ⓐ Ⓑ Ⓒ Ⓓ	11 Ⓐ Ⓑ Ⓒ Ⓓ
3 Ⓐ Ⓑ Ⓒ Ⓓ	6 Ⓐ Ⓑ Ⓒ Ⓓ	9 Ⓐ Ⓑ Ⓒ Ⓓ	12 Ⓐ Ⓑ Ⓒ Ⓓ

LUCKY DUCK TAKES OFF

Linda Ellerbee **considers** herself a lucky duck. For over twenty-five years, she has been a writer, **producer**, and anchorperson of television news shows. In 1986, she won an Emmy **award** for writing the news program "Our World." She's also written a best-selling book about the television business called *And So It Goes*.

In spite of her **success**, some things about television really bother Ellerbee. She thinks that news **programs** should get the story behind the story. Also she wants to listen to **viewers**, not just talk to them. To do the kind of TV she wants to do, Ellerbee started her own production company in 1987, called Lucky Duck Productions.

In 1991, people from Nickelodeon asked her to produce a news program for kids. That's when "Nick News W/5" was born. (The W/5 stands for the five questions **reporters** always ask: *who, what, where, when,* and *why*.)

Ellerbee knows that "kids are smarter than TV," and she proves her point on each **episode** of "Nick News." She **invites** kids to ask the questions and **discuss** the issues.

CONCLUSIONS FOUND

Why did Linda Ellerbee start Lucky Duck Productions?

Check the best answer.

- ○ to make more money
- ○ to do the kind of TV she wanted to do
- ○ because she could not get a job
- ○ for her children

THE AMAZING ALPHABET

☞ In the dictionary, **guide words** at the top of the page mark the first and last entry on that page.

Write the New Words between the correct guide words.

New Words
considers
producer
award
success
programs
viewers
reporters
episode
invites
discuss

accept/guilt

_____

_____

_____

_____

guise/react

_____

_____

_____

read/tail

_____

_____

take/voyage

_____

Need help?
Use the
glossary
on page 103.

WORDS AND MEANINGS—A PERFECT MATCH

☞ **Context clues** are words in a sentence or phrase that help you understand the meaning of a word. Look for context clues to help you match each New Word with its meaning.

Write the correct letter on each line.

____ 1. considers
____ 2. producer
____ 3. award
____ 4. success
____ 5. programs
____ 6. viewers
____ 7. reporters
____ 8. episode
____ 9. invites
____ 10. discuss

a. to talk about something; have a conversation
b. is of the opinion that; believes
c. one in a series of events, adventures, or shows
d. person in charge of a TV show or movie
e. journalists; people who gather and report news
f. prize; gift for excellence
g. watchers, observers
h. the gaining of wealth, fame, praise
i. TV or radio shows; organized presentations
j. makes a request for; asks to participate

NEW WORDS COMPLETE SENTENCES

Use New Words to finish these sentences.

New Words

considers

producer

award

success

programs

viewers

reporters

episode

invites

discuss

1. Daniel has had great _____ as an actor.

2. He won an _____ for his last performance.

3. Irene organizes educational _____ at the hospital.

4. She _____ experts to speak on different subjects.

5. This month they will _____ nutrition.

6. As a TV _____ , Jane has a lot to think about.

7. She is in charge of every _____ .

8. It is her job to make sure all _____ are entertained.

9. The sight of the poor children in Africa made even the newspaper _____ cry.

10. Mike _____ helping hungry children to be the most important part of his job.

GET TO THE ROOT OF IT

A **root word** is a word that is used as a base for making other words. For example, the root word of **incorrectly** is **correct**. The **prefix** <u>in</u> and the **suffix** <u>ly</u> were added to make a new word.

Circle the root of each word below.

1. recovery
2. misread
3. childish
4. comical
5. reordered
6. successful
7. disorderly
8. midsummer

9. unfinished
10. misstated
11. unaffected
12. wooden
13. disapproved
14. childhood
15. freedom
16. doubtful

17. discussion
18. timeless
19. cheerfulness
20. nonpayment
21. exporting
22. hopelessness
23. insincerely
24. limping

CLOSE STUDY REVEALS HIDDEN WORDS

Find the New Words in the puzzle. You will find them vertically, horizontally, and diagonally.

New Words

considers

producer

award

success

programs

viewers

reporters

episode

invites

discuss

S	U	C	C	E	S	S	R	S	A	C	C	S
M	U	D	E	C	L	I	R	M	P	G	O	M
E	P	I	S	O	D	E	A	I	T	A	N	A
R	A	G	C	I	W	I	L	E	N	T	S	R
G	E	U	C	E	S	N	I	I	E	R	I	G
D	O	I	I	E	W	V	A	W	A	R	D	O
T	C	V	O	N	V	I	E	V	E	P	E	R
X	R	E	P	O	R	T	E	R	S	I	R	P
P	R	O	D	U	C	E	R	I	T	A	S	T
D	I	S	C	U	S	S	R	I	O	U	S	E

IS A PICTURE WORTH A THOUSAND WORDS? NOW YOU CAN FIND OUT

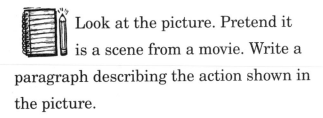 Look at the picture. Pretend it is a scene from a movie. Write a paragraph describing the action shown in the picture.

These questions will help guide your writing:

- What is the movie about?
- Who are the characters?
- What are they doing?
- Why are they doing it?

Use at least four New Words in your paragraph.

 ## TO SEE OR NOT TO SEE

The word *television* comes from the Greek word *tele*, which means "far," and the Latin word *videre*, which means "to see." The word *video* means "I see."

CAT STARS IN EARLY TV SHOW

The first scheduled television programming began in 1936. In July of that year, The Radio Corporation of America (RCA) installed TVs in 150 homes in New York. The National Broadcasting Company (NBC) began sending programs into these homes. The first program shown was a cartoon of Felix the Cat.

READ MORE ABOUT IT

- *In the Newsroom* by April Koral. (Franklin Watts, 1988)
- *On the Air: Behind the Scenes at a TV Newscast* by Esther Rudomin Hautzig. (Macmillan, 1991)
- *Advertising* by Susan Wake. (Garrett Educational Corporation, 1990)

Tune in to the test!

TEST YOUR BEST

When your scored test is returned to you, look over any errors you made. Decide why your answers are incorrect. If you are not sure, ask your teacher to explain.

Read each sentence. Select the answer that best completes each one. Fill in the circle for the answer at the bottom of the page.

1   I watch my favorite TV ____ on Wednesday night.

   A   viewers
   B   reporters
   C   advertisers
   D   programs

2   Linda has had ____ because she has worked hard.

   A   viewers
   B   success
   C   programs
   D   advertisers

3   We need to ____ this matter tomorrow.

   A   discuss
   B   disgust
   C   disguise
   D   dislike

4   This note ____ me to attend the party.

   A   wants
   B   considers
   C   approves
   D   invites

5   The Emmy ____ is given for the best TV programs.

   A   success
   B   episode
   C   award
   D   producer

6   He ____ himself lucky to work at such an exciting job.

   A   invites
   B   helps
   C   proves
   D   considers

Read each set of sentences. Select the word that completes the first sentence according to the stated meaning. Fill in the circle for the answer at the bottom of the page.

7   He is both the ____ and an actor in that movie. Which word indicates that his other role is that of one who is responsible for the movie?

   A   reporters   **C**   viewers
   B   producer   **D**   success

8   I watched my favorite ____ of "Our World" for the fifth time. Which word indicates one in a regular series of shows?

   A   success   **C**   programs
   B   episode   **D**   award

9   Good ____ always tell the truth. Which word indicates people who write and give the news?

   A   viewers   **C**   reporters
   B   producer   **D**   programs

10   Some ____ of TV programs believe everything they see and hear. Which word indicates people who watch TV?

   A   reporters   **C**   raters
   B   producer   **D**   viewers

11   ____ this problem with your parents. Which word indicates you are to talk about the problem with your parents?

   A   Discuss   **C**   Help
   B   Understand   **D**   View

12   I am not sure why I have met with ____ . Which word indicates that the speaker is unsure of why she got the results she hoped for?

   A   award   **C**   reporters
   B   success   **D**   episode

ANSWERS

1	Ⓐ Ⓑ Ⓒ Ⓓ	4	Ⓐ Ⓑ Ⓒ Ⓓ	7	Ⓐ Ⓑ Ⓒ Ⓓ	10	Ⓐ Ⓑ Ⓒ Ⓓ
2	Ⓐ Ⓑ Ⓒ Ⓓ	5	Ⓐ Ⓑ Ⓒ Ⓓ	8	Ⓐ Ⓑ Ⓒ Ⓓ	11	Ⓐ Ⓑ Ⓒ Ⓓ
3	Ⓐ Ⓑ Ⓒ Ⓓ	6	Ⓐ Ⓑ Ⓒ Ⓓ	9	Ⓐ Ⓑ Ⓒ Ⓓ	12	Ⓐ Ⓑ Ⓒ Ⓓ

KWANZAA – CANDLES, CULTURE, AND CREATIVITY

Kwanzaa is a seven-day African American **celebration** held from December 26 to January 1. The holiday was started in 1966 by Dr. Maulana Karenga to remind people of their African **heritage**. It is based on **traditional** African harvest festivals.

African American families and friends celebrate their **culture**, remember **ancestors**, give thanks for the good things of the past year, and think about the future.

The celebration centers around seven **principles**. Each day of Kwanzaa focuses on one of them. They are **unity**, control of your life, working together, sharing money, having a **purpose**, being creative, and having faith.

There are several **symbols** of Kwanzaa. The *mkeka*, a symbol of history, is a woven mat upon which other Kwanzaa items are placed. A cup, the *kikombe cha umoja*, is a symbol of staying together. Fruits and vegetables on the mkeka **represent** the harvest and all work. The *zawadi* are gifts given during Kwanzaa. And the *kinara* is a candleholder with seven candles called *mishumma saba*. One candle is lit each day of Kwanzaa.

DRAW YOUR OWN CONCLUSION

Kwanzaa is centered around seven principles. What is <u>not</u> one of the principles?
Check the best answer.

❑ unity
❑ obtaining goods
❑ having faith
❑ control of your life

ALPHABET ORDERS WORDS

☞ In the dictionary, **guide words** at the top of the page mark the first and last entry on that page.

Write the New Words between the correct guide words below.

New Words

unity
celebration
traditional
heritage
ancestors
principles
purpose
symbols
represent
culture

allow/cure

_____

_____

_____

heart/pursue

_____

_____

_____

record/upward

_____

_____

_____

_____

LOST MEANINGS FOUND! ◆

Use context clues to match each New Word with its meaning.

Write the correct letter on each line.

____ 1. culture

____ 2. represent

____ 3. unity

____ 4. celebration

____ 5. heritage

____ 6. principles

____ 7. ancestors

____ 8. symbols

____ 9. traditional

____ 10. purpose

a. objects that represent something or someone

b. intention or aim

c. that which is passed on through generations in a family or group

d. the ideas, customs, traditions, and values of a group

e. predecessors; earlier generations of family

f. ceremony or festivity to mark an event

g. guiding beliefs

h. handed down; long-established

i. to stand for

j. togetherness; community

WORDS COMPLETE SENTENCES

Use New Words to complete these sentences.

New Words

celebration
traditional
culture
heritage
ancestors
unity
principles
purpose
symbols
represent

1. My mother's _____ immigrated to the United States from Slovakia.

2. The _____ of their journey was to find better jobs.

3. The _____ of Thanksgiving brings many families together.

4. It is _____ to have turkey as part of the holiday.

5. The menorah is one of the _____ of Chanukah.

6. My grandfather taught me about our _____ and religion.

7. Learning is a very important part of my family _____ .

8. Teaching and learning _____ a way to obtain independence.

9. The coach's _____ were very clear.

10. Anyone who broke his rules damaged the _____ of the team, and he would not tolerate that.

PIECES AND PARTS — PUT THEM TOGETHER

A **prefix** is a word part that can be added to the beginning of a root word.

Adding a prefix changes the meaning of the word.

The **prefix** <u>in</u> means <u>not</u>.

Add the prefix <u>in</u> to the root word, and write the new word on the line.

Write a definition for the new word.

ROOT WORD	NEW WORD	MEANING
1. dependent	_____	_____
2. sincere	_____	_____
3. complete	_____	_____
4. visible	_____	_____
5. direct	_____	_____
6. accurate	_____	_____
7. secure	_____	_____
8. expensive	_____	_____
9. considerate	_____	_____
10. divisible	_____	_____

BETWEEN ONE THING AND ANOTHER—ANALOGIES

👉 **Analogies** show the relationships between things.

glove is to **hand** as **sock** is to **foot**

Use a word from the word list to finish each analogy.

1. _____ is to <u>hide</u> as <u>clean</u> is to <u>dirty</u>

2. <u>separate</u> is to <u>diversity</u> as <u>whole</u> is to _____

3. _____ is to <u>building</u> as <u>feet</u> is to <u>person</u>

4. <u>big</u> is to _____ as <u>small</u> is to <u>minor</u>

5. <u>bright</u> is to _____ as <u>shiny</u> is to <u>dull</u>

6. <u>1776</u> is to _____ as <u>1492</u> is to <u>discovery</u>

7. <u>toes</u> is to <u>foot</u> as _____ is to <u>hand</u>

8. _____ is to <u>descendents</u> as <u>before</u> is to <u>after</u>

9. <u>leaves</u> is to <u>tree</u> as _____ is to <u>sheep</u>

10. _____ is to <u>wrist</u> as <u>ring</u> is to <u>finger</u>

Word List
major
wool
ancestors
independence
fingers
faded
seek
bracelet
unity
base

HOW DO YOU CELEBRATE?

Write an essay about one of your favorite holidays or celebrations. Then draw a picture of something that is a symbol of the holiday or celebration.

These questions will help guide your writing:

- What is unique about the holiday or celebration?
- Are there any special traditions that you observe?
- What is your favorite part of the event?

Use at least four New Words in your essay.

WHAT'S IN A NAME?

The word *kwanza* means "first" or "first fruits of harvest" in the east African language of Swahili. The extra *a* in the celebration name gives the word seven letters, one for each of the seven Kwanzaa principles.

THE COLORS OF KWANZAA

Kwanzaa decorations are red, black, and green. Red represents the blood, struggles, and hard work. Black stands for their skin color and beauty, and green represents hope for the future.

KEEP UP WITH KWANZAA!
READ:

- *Imani's Gift at Kwanzaa* by Denise Burden-Patmon. (Modern Curriculum Press, 1992)

- *Kwanzaa* by A.P. Porter. (Carolrhoda Books, 1991)

- *Seven Candles for Kwanzaa* by Andrea Davis Pinkney. (Dial, 1993)

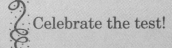 Celebrate the test!

TEST-TAKING SECRETS REVEALED

Be careful of answers that look or sound alike. Say the words to yourself.

Complete each definition with the best word or words. Fill in the circle for the answer at the bottom of the page.

1 To have a <u>purpose</u> means to have a—

   A fish   **C** book
   B reason   **D** cause

2 To follow <u>principles</u> is to follow—

   A beliefs   **C** trucks
   B teachers   **D** goals

3 To celebrate your <u>heritage</u> is to celebrate—

   A birthdays
   B success
   C what you have worked for
   D what has been handed down

4 To <u>represent</u> something is to—

   A like it   **C** reject it
   B stand for it   **D** put it out

5 Something that is <u>traditional</u> is—

   A traded for   **C** handed down
   B sent to   **D** put out

6 To work for <u>unity</u> is to work for—

   A harmony
   B success
   C trust
   D money

Read each set of sentences. Select the word or words that best complete the second sentence in each set. Fill in the circle for the answer at the bottom of the page.

7 The <u>celebration</u> took place at my grandmother's house. <u>Celebration</u> means—

   A a contest   **C** a festivity
   B a test   **D** a meeting

8 It is a feature of our <u>culture</u> to eat lots of fish. <u>Culture</u> means—

   A garden   **C** kinds of food
   B diet   **D** way of life

9 I do not understand all of the <u>symbols</u> that are used. <u>Symbols</u> are objects that—

   A are played
   B stand for other things
   C make a lot of noise
   D are banged together

10 My <u>ancestors</u> came from France. <u>Ancestors</u> means people who are—

   A aunts and uncles
   B before you in a family
   C sons and daughters
   D parents

11 My father voted the way he did because of his <u>principles</u>. <u>Principles</u> are—

   A parties   **C** beliefs
   B clubs   **D** friends

12 The <u>purpose</u> of this exercise is to stretch your muscles. <u>Purpose</u> means—

   A course   **C** path
   B aim   **D** number

ANSWERS

1 Ⓐ Ⓑ Ⓒ Ⓓ	4 Ⓐ Ⓑ Ⓒ Ⓓ	7 Ⓐ Ⓑ Ⓒ Ⓓ	10 Ⓐ Ⓑ Ⓒ Ⓓ
2 Ⓐ Ⓑ Ⓒ Ⓓ	5 Ⓐ Ⓑ Ⓒ Ⓓ	8 Ⓐ Ⓑ Ⓒ Ⓓ	11 Ⓐ Ⓑ Ⓒ Ⓓ
3 Ⓐ Ⓑ Ⓒ Ⓓ	6 Ⓐ Ⓑ Ⓒ Ⓓ	9 Ⓐ Ⓑ Ⓒ Ⓓ	12 Ⓐ Ⓑ Ⓒ Ⓓ

BODY SENDS
MIXED-UP MESSAGES

Did you ever hit your funny bone? It doesn't feel very funny does it? The "funny bone" is actually a nerve near the back of the **elbow**. A **nerve** is like a line that carries messages to your **brain**. If you bump that nerve, those messages get mixed up, and your elbow **tingles**. That feeling **certainly** is not funny.

Another kind of tingling occurs when your arm or leg "falls asleep." If you put on too much **pressure** the wrong way, the arm or leg won't work well. This happens because not enough blood reaches the limb. **Poisonous wastes** build up as the blood flow shuts down. As you try to use your arm or leg, these wastes mix up the nerve messages. You then feel "pins and needles."

The next time your arm or leg falls asleep, don't **worry**! Just shake it gently to get the blood **flowing** properly again. Also, the next time someone you know hits his or her funny bone, you can explain that it isn't a bone. Your friend already knows that it isn't funny!

"It hurt so bad I laughed. I mean I laughed so much it hurt!"
says funny bone.

CONCLUSIONS FLOW FROM TINGLING STORY

Why do you think the story was written?
Check the best answer.

❏ to cause you worry

❏ to scare you

❏ to stop you from hitting your elbow

❏ to teach you something

GUIDE WORDS RELIEVE STRESS

☞ In the dictionary, **guide words** at the top of the page show the first and last entries on the page. All other entries on the page are in alphabetical order between those words.

Write the New Words in alphabetical order under the correct guide words.

New Words

pressure
wastes
flowing
certainly
brain
nerve
elbow
poisonous
tingles
worry

braid/eject

_____

_____

elate/net

_____

_____

new/time

_____

_____

tinfoil/worst

_____

_____

PRESSURE ON TO MATCH WORDS AND MEANINGS

Match each New Word below with its meaning. Write the letter of the meaning on the line next to the word.

Need Help? Check out the glossary on page 103.

____ 1. worry

____ 2. wastes

____ 3. brain

____ 4. tingles

____ 5. flowing

____ 6. poisonous

____ 7. certainly

____ 8. pressure

____ 9. nerve

____ 10. elbow

a. capable of harming or killing by poison

b. moving in a stream as water does

c. materials left over or thrown out as useless

d. the tissue inside the skull of a person or of any animal by which it can think and feel

e. without any doubt; surely

f. to be troubled; feel or make uneasy or anxious

g. a pressing or being pressed; force of pushing or of weight

h. has or gives a prickling or stinging feeling

i. fiber that connects the muscles, glands, or organs with the brain and spinal cord

j. joint where the forearm and upper arm meet

INCOMPLETE SENTENCES KEEP READERS ON
PINS and NEEDLES

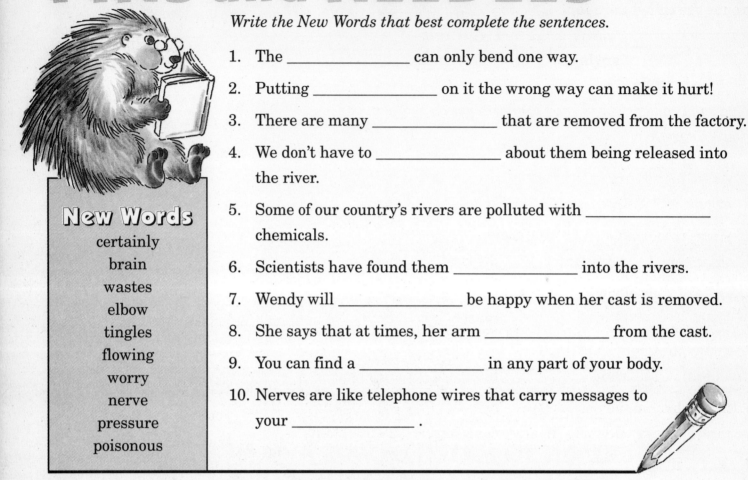

Write the New Words that best complete the sentences.

1. The _____ can only bend one way.

2. Putting _____ on it the wrong way can make it hurt!

3. There are many _____ that are removed from the factory.

4. We don't have to _____ about them being released into the river.

5. Some of our country's rivers are polluted with _____ chemicals.

6. Scientists have found them _____ into the rivers.

7. Wendy will _____ be happy when her cast is removed.

8. She says that at times, her arm _____ from the cast.

9. You can find a _____ in any part of your body.

10. Nerves are like telephone wires that carry messages to your _____ .

New Words

certainly
brain
wastes
elbow
tingles
flowing
worry
nerve
pressure
poisonous

DRAW THE LINE ON HOMONYM CONFUSION

☞ **Homonyms** are words that sound alike but have different meanings and spellings.

fore and **four**   **or** and **oar**

Draw lines to match the homonyms below.

1. waste	sent	6. steal	steel
2. prey	blue	7. hear	tale
3. flour	waist	8. right	through
4. blew	flower	9. tail	write
5. cent	pray	10. threw	here

Use the correct homonyms from above to complete the sentences at the right.

a. Pamela has a red belt around her _____ .

b. A deaf person cannot _____ .

c. The wind _____ the shingles off the roof.

d. I don't think that answer is _____ .

e. Next, you put the _____ in the mixture and stir.

CATEGORIES HELP WORDS GET ORGANIZED

☞ Words can be grouped to show they go together. These groups are called **categories**.

Cats, **dogs**, and **squirrels**

are in the category of <u>animals</u>.

Read each category and circle the three words that can be grouped together.

1. where <u>nerves</u> are found

   arms　　　　legs　　　　shoes　　　　body

2. places to put <u>waste</u>

   trash can　　refrigerator　　disposal　　sewer

3. parts of your <u>elbow</u>

   heart　　　skin　　　muscle　　　bone

4. things that <u>flow</u>

   water　　　soil　　　blood　　　gasoline

5. things that can be <u>poisonous</u>

   insect sprays　cleaning liquids　cauliflower　house plants

6. what you might get when you <u>worry</u>

   nervous　　new tooth　　headache　　upset stomach

7. things controlled by the <u>brain</u>

   sight　　　smell　　　sister　　　speech

HIDDEN BRAIN POWER REVEALED

✎ How does the brain help us? Read about the brain in an encyclopedia or another book. Write a short report about the brain. Then draw a picture of the brain and label the parts.

Think about these questions before you begin to write.

• What are the parts of the brain?

• What makes up the brain?

• What happens if the brain is injured?

Use at least four New Words in your report.

TRY THESE BOOKS THAT WILL TICKLE YOUR FANCY

• *The Magic School Bus, Inside the Human Body* by Joanna Cole. (Scholastic, 1989)
• *Outside and Inside You* by Sandra Markle. (Bradbury Press, 1991)
• *Why Do Our Bodies Stop Growing?* by Philip Whitfield. (Viking Kestrel, 1988)

LEAVE YOUR MESSAGE AFTER THE BEEP

Have you noticed when you hit your funny bone that only your pinkie and your ring finger feel pain and become numb? Thank goodness the other three fingers don't get the message!

HAVE YOU EVER FELT NERVE - LESS?

The only animals without nerves in their bodies are sponges and single-celled creatures like amebas.

You've got the nerve to take the test!

SCORE HIGHER ON TESTS

Look over your test a last time to make sure you did not miss any questions and that your answers can be easily read by the teacher.

Read each group of words. Select the answer that means the same as the underlined word. Fill in the circle for the answer at the bottom of the page.

1 worry about a test
- **A** think
- **B** feel uneasy
- **C** feel sick
- **D** talk

2 arm tingles
- **A** prickles
- **B** hurts
- **C** itches
- **D** aches

3 hit a nerve
- **A** sore muscle
- **B** spinal cord
- **C** string
- **D** connecting fiber

4 certainly will try
- **A** maybe
- **B** usually
- **C** surely
- **D** never

5 hurt his elbow
- **A** arm joint
- **B** knee joint
- **C** wrist joint
- **D** finger joint

6 apply some pressure
- **A** force
- **B** medicine
- **C** bandage
- **D** action

Read the paragraphs. Select the words that best fit in the blanks. Fill in the circles for the answers at the bottom of the page.

Have you ever cut or burned your finger? The pain you __7__ felt was due to messages that were being sent by some __8__ in the area. Your __9__ received these messages and told you that the cut or burn hurt.

7
- **A** almost
- **B** unlikely
- **C** certainly
- **D** never

8
- **A** bones
- **B** nerves
- **C** elbows
- **D** fingers

9
- **A** elbow
- **B** nerve
- **C** finger
- **D** brain

__10__ materials can sometimes build up in the muscles. One of the jobs of the blood as it is __11__ through the body is to get rid of these __12__.

10
- **A** Poisonous
- **B** Pressure
- **C** Worried
- **D** Hard

11
- **A** certainly
- **B** flowing
- **C** walking
- **D** pressure

12
- **A** wastes
- **B** hurts
- **C** tingles
- **D** aches

ANSWERS

1	A B C D	4	A B C D	7	A B C D	10	A B C D
2	A B C D	5	A B C D	8	A B C D	11	A B C D
3	A B C D	6	A B C D	9	A B C D	12	A B C D

GLOSSARY

Pronunciation Key

Letters	Show the Sound of	Written as
a	cat	KAT
ah	odd	AHD
ahr	bar	BAHR
aw	lawn	LAWN
ay	pay	PAY
b	bib	BIB
ch	chip	CHIP
d	deed	DEED
e	pet	PET
ee	bee	BEE
er	care	KER
eye	island	EYE luhnd
f	fast	FAST
g	gag	GAG
h	hat	HAT
i	pit	PIT
ir	dear	DIR
j	joke	JOHK
k	kit	KIT
l	lid	LID
m	man	MAN
n	no	NOH
ng	thing	THING
oh	go	GOH
oo	moon	MOON
or	store	STOR
ow	out	OWT
oy	joy	JOY
p	pop	PAHP
r	rat	RAT
s	see	SEE
sh	ship	SHIP
t	tin	TIN
th	thing	THING
th	then	THEN
u	book	BUK
uh	cut	KUHT
ur	her	HUR
v	vase	VAYS
w	with	WITH
y	yet	YET
z	zebra	ZEE bruh
zh	vision	VIZH uhn

A a

ac•claimed (ah KLAYMD) *v.* given high praise

a•chieve•ments (ah CHEEV ments) *n.* goals reached or accomplished

an•ces•tors (AN ses terz) *n.* predecessors; earlier generations of family

ap•par•el (ah PER el) *n.* coverings for the body, usually made of fabric; clothing

ap•pear•ance (ah PIR ens) *n.* the way a person or thing looks

ap•proach•es (ah PROHCH ez) *v.* comes closer or draws nearer

ar•chi•tect (AHR ki tekt) *n.* person who designs buildings and other structures

a•re•na (ah REE nah) *n.* a stadium or amphitheater; a place where public events are held

as•pire (uh SPEYER) *v.* to desire to achieve a goal

as•sem•ble (ah SEM buhl) *v.* to put together the parts of

as•tro•nauts (AS trah nawts) *n.* people who travel in outer space

at•tached (ah TACHD) *v.* fastened or joined together by sticking or tying

at•tacks (ah TAKS) *n.* actions against another that are intended to harm

au•to•mat•ic (AWT uh MAT ik) *adj.* moving or working by itself

av•a•lanche (AV uh lanch) *n.* a large mass of snow, ice, or rocks sliding swiftly down a mountain

a•ward (ah WORD) *n.* prize; gift for excellence

B b

back•wards (BAK wordz) *adv.* in the direction opposite from which one is facing

bald (BAWLD) *adj.* having no hair on all or part of the scalp

barb•wire (BAHRB WEYER) *n.* wire with sharp points along it, used for fences or barriers

brain (BRAYN) *n.* the tissue inside the skull of a person or of any animal by which it can think and feel

bur•y (BER ee) *v.* to cover up so as to hide

C c

camp•ers (KAM perz) *n.* people who vacation at a camp, often in forested or undeveloped areas

cat•a•pults (KAT ah puhlts) *v.* throws or launches an object

cat•tle (KAT uhl) **pl.n.** cows and bulls

cel•e•bra•tion (sel uh BRAY shuhn) *n.* ceremony or festivity to mark an event

cen•tu•ry (SEN chuhr ee) *n.* a time period lasting 100 years

cer•tain•ly (SURT uhn lee) *adv.* without any doubt; surely

check (CHEK) *v.* in hockey, to block an opponent

chis•eled (CHIZ uhld) *v.* shaped or carved with a chisel

choic•es (CHOYS ez) *n.* possibilities to be selected from

chores (CHORZ) *n.* common tasks that have to be done

cir•cling (SUR kling) *v.* moving around in a circle

cir•cu•lar (SUR kyu ler) *adj.* moving in a circle

cleansed (KLENZD) *v.* removed of dirt or other impurities

coaxed (KOHKSD) *v.* persuaded by praise or promises

com•bines (kuhm BEYENZ) *v.* brings together; joins; unites

com•pe•ti•tions (kahm pe TISH uhnz) *n.* contests

com•pli•cat•ed (KAHM pli kayt ed) *adj.* not simple

con•sid•ers (kuhn SID erz) *v.* is of the opinion that; believes

con•sis•ten•cy (kuhn SIS ten see) *n.* conformity over time; evenness

con•trolled (kuhn TROHLD) *v.* ruled, guided, or managed

course (KORS) *n.* a route or direction of movement

cov•et•ed (KUHV et ed) *adj.* greatly wanted or desired

co•zy (KOH zee) *adj.* warm and comfortable; snug

cre•at•ing (kree AYT ing) *v.* making or bringing something into being

crew (KROO) *n.* a group of people working together

cul•ture (KUL cher) *n.* the ideas, customs, traditions, and values of a group

D d

dan•ger•ous (DAYN jer uhs) *adj.* full of danger; likely to cause injury or pain

death (DETH) *n.* the act or fact of dying; ending of life

de•fen•sive (dee FEN siv) *adj.* with the intent of preventing attack or protecting something

de•grees (di GREEZ) *n.* units used in measuring temperature that are shown by the symbol °

di•gests (di JESTS) *v.* changes or breaks down food into a form that can be used by the body

dis•cuss (di SKUHS) *v.* to talk about something; have a conversation

driv•ing (DREYEV ing) *v.* leading or forcing to go in a certain direction

dull (DUHL) *adj.* not interesting; boring

du•ty (DYUT ee) *n.* thing that is done as a part of a person's work; what is required

E e

el•bow (EL boh) *n.* the joint where the forearm and upper arm meet

em•bar•rassed (em BER ast) *v.* feeling self-conscious or uncomfortable

en•e•my (EN uh mee) *n.* a person, animal, or group that hates or fights against another

ep•i•sode (EP uh sohd) *n.* one in a series of events, adventures, or shows

ex•change (eks CHAYNJ) *v.* to give in return for something else; trade

ex•cit•ing (ek SEYET ing) *adj.* stimulating or thrilling

ex•plor•ing (ek SPLOR ing) *n.* the act of traveling in a region that is not well-known to find out more about it

ex•tinct (ek STINGT) *adj.* no longer living; having died out

F f

fa•mous (FAY muhs) *adj.* well-known

fash•ion (FASH uhn) *n.* the current style, usually changes over time

fa•vor•ite (FAY ver it) *n.* the one preferred or liked best

fear•less (FIR les) *adj.* brave; unafraid

fes•ti•vals (FES ti vuhlz) *n.* days or times of feasting or celebrating; happy holidays

few (FYOO) *adj.* not many; a small number of

flow•ing (FLOH ing) *v.* moving in a stream as water does

for•mer (FOR mer) *adj.* past; earlier

fre•quent•ly (FREE kwent lee) *adv.* often; repeatedly

fright (FREYET) *n.* sudden fear; alarm

fu•ture (FYOO cher) *n.* time that is to come; time after the present time

G g

gas•e•ous (GAS ee uhs) *adj.* made of, or like, gas

gath•ers (GATH erz) *v.* brings or comes together in one place

gift•ed (GIFT ed) *adj.* having special talents or skills

gi•gan•tic (jeye GAN tic) *adj.* huge; immense; very large

gla•ciers (GLAY shers) *n.* large masses of ice and snow that move very slowly down a mountain or across land

goal (GOHL) *n.* in hockey, the area into which the puck must be hit to score a point; the act of getting the puck in this area

goug•es (GOWJ ez) *n.* cuts or grooves in smooth surfaces

grav•i•ty (GRAV it ee) *n.* force that pulls things toward the center of Earth

growl•ing (GROWL ing) *v.* making a rumbling, menacing sound

gur•gling (GUR gling) *adj.* making a bubbling or rippling sound

H h

her•i•tage (HER i tij) *n.* that which is passed on through generations in a family or group

I i

i•de•al (eye DEE uhl) *adj.* exactly as one would wish; perfect

il•lus•tri•ous (i LUHS tree uhs) *adj.* outstanding; characterized by greatness

i•mag•ine (i MAJ in) *v.* to make up a picture or idea in the mind; form an idea of

im•por•tant (im PORT nt) *adj.* significant or meaningful

in•for•ma•tion (in for MAY shun) *n.* facts or knowledge about something

in•structs (in STRUKTS) *v.* gives information; teaches

in•tel•li•gence (in TEL i jens) *n.* the ability to learn and understand, or to solve problems

in•tes•tines (in TES tinz) *n.* the long, winding organs of digestion

in•ven•tor (in VEN ter) *n.* a person who devises a new tool or process

in•vites (in VEYETS) *v.* makes a request for; asks to participate

J j

juic•es (JYOOS ez) *n.* liquids

L l

ledge (LEJ) *n.* a flat, narrow shelf that comes out from a cliff or wall

liq•uid (LIK wid) *n.* a substance that flows easily; matter that is neither a solid nor a gas

lis•tens (LIS uhnz) *v.* hears and is alert to something in the environment

M m

med•als (MED uhlz) *n.* objects, often flat pieces of metal, awarded for achievement

me•mo•ri•al (me MOR ee ahl) *n.* a structure built to remember a person or group of people

mis•sile (MIS uhl) *n.* an object made to be thrown or shot at a target

mold•ing (MOHL ding) *v.* forming or shaping

mon•sters (MAHN sterz) *n.* huge animals or things

mus•cles (MUHS uhlz) *n.* the tissues in an animal's body that can be stretched or tightened to move the parts of the body

mu•se•um (myoo ZEE uhm) *n.* a building or room for keeping and showing objects important in history, science, or art

N n

nerve (NURV) *n.* fiber that connects the muscles, glands, or organs with the brain and spinal cord

O o

o•vals (OH vuhlz) *n.* things shaped like an egg or like an ellipse

own•ers (OHN erz) *n.* the rightful possessors of something

P p

pas•sen•gers (PAS en jerz) *n.* persons traveling in a car, bus, plane, or other vehicle, but not helping to operate it

pen•al•ty (PEN uhl tee) *n.* punishment for breaking a rule or law

plains (PLAYNZ) *n.* large stretches of flat land

poi•son•ous (POY zuh nuhs) *adj.* capable of harming or killing by poison

pol•ished (PAHL ishd) *v.* made smooth and shiny

pop•u•lar (PAHP yuh ler) *adj.* liked by many people

pot•ter•y (PAHT er ee) *n.* dishes, pots, and bowls made of clay

pres•sure (PRESH uhr) *n.* a pressing or being pressed; force of pushing or of weight

prev•a•lent (PREV uh luhnt) *adj.* widespread; common; preferred

prin•ci•ples (PRIN suh puhls) *n.* guiding beliefs

pris•on (PRIZ uhn) *n.* a place where people or things are shut up

pro•duc•er (pruh DYOOS er) *n.* person in charge of a TV show or movie

pro•grams (PROH gramz) *n.* TV or radio shows; organized presentations

pro•tect (proh TEKT) *v.* to guard or defend against harm or danger; shield

pur•pose (PUR puhs) *n.* intention or aim

Q q

quick•sand (KWIK sand) *n.* loose, wet sand not firm enough to stand on

quite (KWEYET) *adv.* very or somewhat; rather

R r

range (RAYNJ) *n.* a large open grazing area for cattle and livestock

raw (RAW) *adj.* not cooked

re•cord•ed (ree KORD ed) *v.* written down for future use; kept account of

rec•ords (REK ohrdz) *n.* accounts of activities and events

re•main (ree MAYN) *v.* to go on being; continue

re•port•ers (ree PORT erz) *n.* journalists; people who gather and report news

rep•re•sent (rep ree ZENT) *v.* to stand for

res•cue (RES kyoo) *v.* to free from danger or evil

re•search (REE surch) *n.* careful study to find out facts and principles about a subject

re•spon•si•ble (ree SPAHN suh bel) *adj.* held accountable for; in charge of

rink (RINK) *n.* an area for skating

risks (RISKS) *n.* chances of getting hurt, or of losing; danger

roamed (ROHMD) *v.* traveled about with no special plan or purpose; wandered

S s

sci•en•tists (SEYE en tists) *n.* experts in science, such as a chemists or biologists

sculp•tures (SKUHLP chers) *n.* carved, cut, and designed objects

shal•low (SHAL oh) *adj.* not deep

shares (SHERZ) *v.* gives out knowledge, material, or other resources

shaves (SHAYVZ) *v.* removes thin layers by cutting

shel•ters (SHEL terz) *n.* places or things that cover or protect, as from the weather or danger

shield (SHEELD) *n.* something that guards or protects, as a safety guard over machinery

shy (SHEYE) *adj.* easily frightened; timid

sig•nal (SIG nuhl) *v.* to give a sign that warns, directs, or informs

si•lenced (SEYE lensd) *v.* made silent; made still

sim•u•la•tor (SIM yu layt er) *n.* a machine that approximates the conditions found in a particular situation

skate (SKAYT) *v.* to slide along the ice on metal blades

skel•e•ton (SKEL e ten) *n.* the framework of bones of an animal's body

slick (SLIK) *adj.* slippery and wet; smooth

sniff (SNIF) *v.* to take in short breaths through the nose as when trying to smell something

soaked (SOHKD) *v.* put in water or other liquid for a thorough wetting

soar•ing (SOR ing) *v.* rising or flying in the air

soil (SOYL) *n.* the top layer of earth in which plants grow; ground

spines (SPEYENZ) *n.* thin, sharp, or stiff parts that stick out on certain plants and animals

spi•ral (SPEYE rel) *adj.* circling around a center in a curve

spo•rad•ic (spah RAD ik) *adj.* uneven or inconsistent

squirt (SKWURT) *v.* to force or shoot a liquid in a narrow stream

starved (STAHRVD) *v.* deprived of food

steep (STEEP) *adj.* slanting sharply up or

down; having a sharp slope

steer (STIR) *v.* to guide by means of a rudder or wheel; direct the movement of

stom•ach (STUHM ik) *n.* a muscular organ connected to the esophagus that digests food

sto•ry•tell•er (STOHR ee TEL er) *n.* person who tells histories, tales, and stories to others

stout (STOWT) *adj.* strong; sturdy; thick

streak (STREEK) *v.* to move at a very fast speed

strug•gle (STRUHG uhl) *v.* to try or work very hard; strive

stu•di•o (STOO dee oh) *n.* the workplace of an artist or a designer

studs (STUHDZ) *n.* raised knobs or projections used to prevent sliding on slippery surfaces

style (STEYEL) *n.* particular way of living or doing things

suc•cess (suhk SES) *n.* the gaining of wealth, fame, praise

sur•face (SUR fis) *n.* the outside or outer facing of a thing

sur•viv•al (suhr VEYE vahl) *n.* the act or fact of continuing to exist

swamps (SWAHMPS) *n.* pieces of wet or spongy land; marshes

sym•bols (SIM buhlz) *n.* objects that represent something or someone

T t

tame (TAYM) *v.* overcome the wildness of; make gentle

tan•gling (TANG gling) *v.* becoming knotted, twisted, or confused

tar•get (TAHR get) *n.* a thing aimed at, as in shooting a rifle or arrow

tem•per•a•ture (TEM pre chuhr) *n.* the degree of hotness or coldness, usually measured by a thermometer

tend (TEND) *v.* watch over; take care of

ten•ta•cles (TEN tah kelz) *n.* long, slender parts of some animals used for feeling, gripping, or moving

tin•gles (TING guhls) *v.* has or gives a prickling or stinging feeling

trace (TRAYS) *v.* to draw an outline

tra•di•tion•al (trah DISH uh nel) *adj.* handed down; long-established

trop•i•cal (TRAHP i kel) *adj.* from the region

of the earth that is noted for its hot climate

U u

un•de•ni•a•ble (uhn dee NEYE ah buhl) *adj.* without dispute or disagreement

un•der•neath (un der NEETH) *prep.* under; below; beneath

u•nique (yu NEEK) *adj.* highly unusual; rare

u•ni•ty (YOON i tee) *n.* togetherness; community

V v

val•ued (VAL yud) *v.* given much importance; highly thought of

ve•hi•cle (VEE i kel) *n.* something that carries persons or things over land or in space, such as an automobile or a spacecraft

view•ers (VYOO erz) *n.* watchers, observers

W w

wastes (WAYSTS) *n.* materials left over or thrown out as useless

wea•ry (WIR ee) *adj.* tired; worn out

weight•less (WAYT les) *adj.* without the pull of gravity

wor•ry (WUR ee) *v.* to be troubled; feel or make uneasy or anxious

Z z

ze•ro (ZIR oh) *adj.* nothing; the base point number

Answer Key

Slap Shot Sends Puck Soaring
pages 3-7

Detail Check
Canada

Alphabet Keeps Words in Order
1. backwards
2. check
3. defensive
4. exciting
5. fearless
6. goal
7. missile
8. penalty
9. skate
10. streak

Words and Meanings Team Up for Exciting Match
1. b
2. d
3. e
4. c
5. h
6. i
7. g
8. f
9. j
10. a

Completed Sentences Score Big
1. exciting
2. streak
3. goal
4. penalty
5. Defensive
6. fearless
7. missile
8. check
9. skate
10. backwards

Multiple Meanings Make Words Mean More
1. a
2. b
3. b
4. a
5. b
6. a
7. a
8. b

The Truth About Categories
1. hockey players, figure skaters, speed skaters
2. touchdown, home run, basket
3. the lights, the door, the weather
4. car, skater, jet
5. basketball, football, hockey

Test-taking Secrets Revealed
1. A
2. B
3. C
4. A
5. C
6. D
7. A
8. C
9. C
10. B
11. A
12. B

No Bones About It
pages 13-17

What Was That Number Again?
eight

The Amazing Alphabet
1. dangerous
2. death
3. enemy
4. gathers
5. liquid
6. muscles
7. shy
8. silenced
9. skeleton
10. tentacles

Remedy for Meaningless Words
1. d
2. i
3. g
4. a
5. h
6. b
7. e
8. c
9. j
10. f

Incomplete Sentences Cloud the Issue
1. silenced
2. shy
3. gathers
4. tentacles
5. skeleton
6. muscles
7. liquid
8. enemy
9. dangerous
10. death

Antonyms Make a Difference in Meaning
1. liquid
2. death
3. dangerous
4. shy
5. enemy

Get the Picture?
1. skeleton
2. silenced
3. gathers
4. tentacles
5. liquid
6. muscles

Test-day Tips Told
1. C
2. A
3. D
4. B
5. D
6. B
7. C
8. A
9. B
10. D
11. C
12. D

This Plant Bites
pages 8-12

Detail Digest
Insects like to eat the Venus' flytrap.

Words Need Alphabet to Stay in Order
1. cozy
2. digests
3. few
4. ovals
5. popular
6. prison
7. raw
8. signal
9. soil
10. spines

Matching Words with Meanings—It's a Snap
1. e
2. h
3. b
4. j
5. i
6. a
7. c
8. f
9. g
10. d

Missing Words Captured
1. cozy
2. digests
3. soil
4. raw
5. signal
6. few
7. ovals
8. spines
9. prison
10. popular

Speaking of Synonyms . . .
1. raw
2. popular
3. few
4. spines
5. prison
6. cozy
7. ovals
8. soil

Between One Thing and Another—Analogies
1. soil
2. ovals
3. raw
4. spines
5. prison

Score Higher on Tests
1. B
2. C
3. D
4. A
5. A
6. B
7. D
8. C
9. D
10. A
11. C
12. B

The More Names Change—The More They Stay the Same
pages 18-22

Getting the Details
Debbie

Alphabet Is Top Choice For Word Order
1. apparel
2. century
3. choices
4. fashion
5. favorite
6. frequently
7. prevalent
8. quite
9. style
10. unique

Words and Meanings Match Up Perfectly!
1. b
2. d
3. f
4. g
5. i
6. h
7. e
8. c
9. a
10. j

Completed Sentences Are Everybody's Favorite
1. fashion
2. quite
3. style
4. unique
5. choices
6. favorite
7. prevalent
8. century
9. Apparel
10. frequently

Nothing Unusual
act, or
art, ist
sing, er
collect, or
fish, er
cartoon, ist
invent, or
play, er

Mixed-Up Words Need Help
1. unique
2. apparel
3. prevalent
4. style
5. favorite
6. quite
7. fashion
8. frequently
9. century
10. choices

Improve Your Score
1. B
2. A
3. B
4. C
5. B
6. D
7. C
8. D
9. B
10. B
11. B
12. C

African American Cowboys Help Tame the Wild West
pages 23-27

Main Idea Found in Story
African American cowboys

Alphabet Keeps Words in Order
1. barbwire
2. cattle
3. driving
4. former
5. quicksand
6. range
7. responsible
8. tame
9. tend
10. valued

Words and Meanings Tend to Match
1. i
2. b
3. d
4. f
5. g
6. e
7. h
8. j
9. a
10. c

Complete Sentences Valued by Readers
1. former
2. range
3. tend
4. cattle
5. valued
6. quicksand
7. Barbwire
8. responsible
9. driving
10. tame

Root Words Reform, Form New Words
1. dark
2. act
3. north
4. spell
5. former
6. close
7. count
8. need
9. paint
10. fiction
11. tame
12. grace
13. change
14. break
15. music
16. year
17. use
18. tend
19. circle
20. slow
21. appear
22. friend
23. day
24. call

Can You Tame the Wild Puzzle?
Across
2. cattle
4. responsible
5. tend
7. tame
8. quicksand
9. driving
Down
1. barbwire
3. former
4. range
6. valued

Secrets to Success on Tests
1. C
2. A
3. B
4. B
5. B
6. D
7. B
8. C
9. B
10. C
11. B
12. D

Zamboni—Monster of a Machine!
pages 33-37

Finding Main Idea Is Not a Slick Trick
The Zamboni is a machine for smoothing ice on skating rinks.

Alphabet Puts Words on Ice
bank
circling
farm
gigantic
gouges
hot
inventor
night
owners
party
rink
sand
shaves
slick
spiral
studs

Words and Meanings Match
1. f
2. d
3. h
4. i
5. b
6. g
7. c
8. e
9. a
10. j

Sentence Gouges Gone
1. studs
2. rink
3. gouges
4. spiral
5. shaves
6. slick
7. inventor
8. owners
9. gigantic
10. circling

Understanding Antonyms
1. gigantic
2. oppose
3. owners
4. inventor
5. slick
6. gouges
7. bold
8. worse

Categories Are Really Gigantic Word Groups
1. ice, face, wood
2. ice, soap, wax
3. Thomas Edison
   George Washington Carver
   the Wright Brothers
4. mountain, skyscraper, dinosaur
5. shoe, tire, Zamboni
6. merry-go-round, planet, moon

Test-taking Secrets Revealed
1. C
2. D
3. A
4. B
5. A
6. C
7. D
8. C
9. C
10. D
11. B
12. A

Robots Ease Work Woes
pages 28-32

Story Explorers Find Main Idea
Robots can work for people.

Alphabet Makes Word Order Automatic
1. assemble
2. automatic
3. chores
4. complicated
5. controlled
6. dull
7. exploring
8. future
9. instructs
10. weary

Words Are Meaning Machines
1. e
2. h
3. a
4. i
5. f
6. j
7. c
8. g
9. d
10. b

Incomplete Sentences Do Not Compute
1. chores
2. weary
3. automatic
4. controlled
5. assemble
6. complicated
7. dull
8. exploring
9. instructs
10. future

Prefixes Make Word Connections
1. reassemble
2. discomfort
3. rework
4. refill
5. disorder
6. disconnect
7. recount
8. disapprove

Word Search Soon To Be Under Control
```
C H D O R E M A F T I C E
D D U L L W E R U R Y H X
C O M P L I C A T E D O P
E D I S O L T R U C T R L
T R N C O M P W R C O E O
W A S S E M B L E U C S R
S A T U T R E X L A I C I
L O R E T R P E D O R E N
L D U L R L M P U T E Y G
I N C C O N T R O L L E D
M R T R U T E D L I C A O
C O S C N T R L M B L E T
M A U T O M A T I C T O R
```

Secrets to Success on Tests
1. B
2. A
3. D
4. C
5. B
6. A
7. D
8. C
9. C
10. B
11. A
12. C

Growling Stomach Disturbs Class
pages 38-42

Main Idea Uncovered
why your stomach growls

Alphabet Keeps Words in Order
caring
combines
creating
embarrassed
formula
growling
gurgling
intestines
juices
salivate
squirt
starved
stomach

Meanings Revealed
1. f
2. g
3. c
4. a
5. d
6. b
7. i
8. e
9. j
10. h

Missing Words Found
1. gurgling
2. squirt
3. stomach
4. embarrassed
5. growling
6. starved
7. combines
8. intestines
9. juices
10. Creating

Solve the Homonym Puzzle
1. peace-piece
2. feet-feat
3. seam-seem
4. whole-hole
5. son-sun
6. soar-sore
7. weight-wait
8. pale-pail
9. board-bored
10. week-weak
11. weight
12. peace
13. bored
14. seam
15. board
16. soar
17. hole
18. feet
19. weak
20. piece

Don't Get Your Signals Crossed
Across
2. creating
4. gurgling
5. stomach
6. squirt
8. embarrassed
9. starved
Down
1. growling
2. combines
3. juices
7. intestines

Score Higher on Tests
1. A
2. B
3. B
4. D
5. C
6. A
7. A
8. D
9. A
10. C
11. D
12. C

Condors Struggle to Survive
pages 43-47

Sequence Keeps Story on Target
The condor had little to eat.

The Amazing Alphabet
apparent	remain
appearance	*soap*
approaches	soaring
bald	*strange*
ball	struggle
extend	survival
extinct	*tardy*
protect	target
provide	

Words and Meanings Match
1. i	6. j
2. f	7. c
3. a	8. b
4. d	9. g
5. e	10. h

Words Fill Incomplete Sentences
1. extinct
2. survival
3. soaring
4. struggle
5. bald
6. appearance
7. target
8. remain
9. approaches
10. protect

Meanings Change with Suffixes
1. d	6. g
2. e	7. i
3. a	8. j
4. c	9. f
5. b	10. h

Words Scramble for Meaning
1. soaring
2. remain
3. target
4. appearance
5. bald
6. protect
7. extinct
8. approaches
9. struggle
10. survival

Test-day Tips Told
1. B
2. C
3. B
4. A
5. D
6. C
7. B
8. C
9. A
10. C
11. D
12. B

Old Fossils Give Visitors a Fright
pages 48-52

Is Everything in Order?
4, 3, 1, 2

Alphabet Keeps Words from Roaming
ashes	museum
attacks	*mushroom*
attend	roamed
friend	*shake*
fright	shallow
imagine	shield
monsters	*stone*
month	stout
muscle	swamps
	swan

Match Words and Meanings
1. i	6. j
2. a	7. f
3. g	8. d
4. c	9. e
5. h	10. b

Missing Words Unearthed
1. museum	6. attacks
2. shield	7. imagine
3. fright	8. stout
4. monsters	9. roamed
5. swamps	10. shallow

Syllables Cut Monster Words Down to Size
1. shal low
2. i mag ine
3. mon ster
4. at tack
5. mu se um
6. di no saur
7. pro tect
8. gi ant
9. mil lion
10. an i mal

Analogies Form Meaningful Relationships
1. swamp	6. stout
2. shallow	7. smell
3. fright	8. run
4. monster	9. beginning
5. museum	10. pork

Improve Your Score
1. C	7. D
2. D	8. D
3. A	9. B
4. D	10. D
5. C	11. C
6. C	12. A

Storyteller Found Buried in Clay
pages 53-57

The Truth About Cochiti Pottery
The Cochiti people have many written records of their history.

The Amazing Alphabet
boat	polished
cleansed	pottery
important	records
line	*shale*
listens	shares
molding	soaked
paper	storyteller

Meanings Brought to Light
1. g	6. f
2. d	7. b
3. h	8. a
4. c	9. e
5. i	10. j

Missing Words Recovered
1. storyteller	6. important
2. listens	7. molding
3. records	8. cleansed
4. soaked	9. polished
5. shares	10. pottery

There's a New Ending to This Word
1. championship
2. leadership
3. lordship
4. authorship
5. kinship
6. professorship
7. horsemanship
8. apprenticeship
9. marksmanship
10. sportsmanship
11. state of being champion
12. skill as a leader
13. rank of lord
14. state of being an author
15. state of being kin
16. rank of professor
17. skill as a horseman
18. rank of apprentice
19. skill as a marksman
20. skill as a sportsman

Words Lost in a Sea of Letters!
```
L R E C O R D S N G E S
L C U P O T T E R Y T G
T I I S W J E U R O S J
Y C P N F U A S R I C G
P A M E S Y B Y S H W N
B G K T N A T R O P M I
S Q I S P E C I A L L D
H S B I L A S M K T X L
A Z L L R Z B P E Y D O
R L E B Q E P O D M N M
E R X D E H S I L O P R
S F G O C L E A N S E D
```

Secrets to Success on Tests
1. B	7. B
2. D	8. A
3. A	9. D
4. C	10. C
5. C	11. B
6. B	12. C

Hot Air Lifts Balloon!
pages 58-62

Which comes first?
4, 2, 3, 1

Dictionary Lifts Words to New Heights!
attached	passengers
attention	*past*
crest	risks
crew	*steam*
exchange	steer
festivals	tangling
inflame	vehicle
information	*wagon*

Discover the Hidden Meanings
1. e	6. d
2. c	7. j
3. b	8. f
4. g	9. a
5. i	10. h

Lost Words Drop Out of Sky!
1. information	6. passengers
2. steer	7. vehicle
3. risks	8. festivals
4. exchange	9. attached
5. crew	10. tangling

The Shocking Truth About Prefixes
1. misinformation	d
2. misjudge	g
3. misplace	b
4. misstep	a
5. misspell	h
6. mismatch	c
7. misadventure	f
8. misuse	e
9. mistreat	j
10. misunderstand	i

Categories
1. money, toys, stories
2. truck, tractor, plane
3. string, stickers, tape
4. singing, dancing, laughing
5. bicycle, sled, car
6. train, bus, jet
7. encyclopedia, newspaper, magazine

Score Higher on Tests
1. C	7. C
2. C	8. D
3. A	9. A
4. B	10. B
5. D	11. B
6. A	12. D

This Dog Rescues Hikers
pages 63-67

Is That a Fact?
1. F
2. O
3. O
4. F

Alphabet Avalanche

available	intelligence
avalanche	ledge
burst	rescue
bury	*research*
duty	*snicker*
ideal	sniff
identify	steep
intake	underneath

Perfect Match Found Between Words and Meanings
1. c
2. e
3. g
4. j
5. a
6. d
7. i
8. f
9. b
10. h

Missing Words Rescued

steep	duty
sniff	ledge
bury	rescue
ideal	avalanche
underneath	intelligence

Learn to Spot Words with Multiple Meanings
1. 2
2. 1
3. 2
4. 1
5. 1
6. 2

Are Pictures Worth a Thousand Words?
1. ledge
2. bury
3. rescue
4. sniff
5. underneath
6. avalanche

Secrets to Success on Tests
1. B
2. C
3. A
4. D
5. B
6. C
7. B
8. C
9. B
10. D
11. B
12. B

And the Winner Is ... Maya Lin
pages 68-72

Give Me the Facts
1. O
2. F
3. O
4. F

Give These Words Some Order, Please!

apple / chute
architect
arena
chiseled
coin / farmer
competitions
famous
mechanic / memory
medals
memorial
sail / track
sculptures
studio
trace

Meanings Revealed
1. j
2. i
3. h
4. a
5. g
6. d
7. f
8. c
9. b
10. e

Missing Words Found
1. studio
2. competitions
3. architect
4. arena
5. famous
6. sculptures
7. chiseled
8. trace
9. medals
10. memorial

Working with Syl•la•bles
1. me mo ri al
2. fa mous
3. med als
4. stu di o
5. sculp tures
6. chis eled
7. a re na
8. ar chi tect
9. com pe ti tions
10. con ven tion

Between One Thing and Another—Analogies
1. chiseled
2. studio
3. arena
4. sculptures
5. competitions
6. famous
7. trace
8. medals

Test-taking Secrets Revealed
1. A
2. B
3. C
4. C
5. D
6. C
7. A
8. C
9. D
10. B
11. A
12. B

Nolan Ryan— Strike-Out King
pages 73-77

Put the Story in Order
4, 2, 3, 1

The Amazing Alphabet
able / attitude
acclaimed
achievements
aspire
catch / deny
coaxed
consistency
coveted
gall / import
gifted
illustrious
soccer / union
sporadic
undeniable

Meanings Brought to Light
1. e
2. f
3. b
4. i
5. g
6. h
7. c
8. j
9. d
10. a

Missing Word Alert
1. aspire
2. illustrious
3. gifted
4. undeniable
5. acclaimed
6. achievements
7. coaxed
8. coveted
9. sporadic
10. consistency

Working with Synonyms and Antonyms
1. power, weakness
2. support, discourage
3. usual, irregular
4. pal, enemy
5. fail, win
6. begin, finish

Solve This Puzzle
Across
1. undeniable
4. sporadic
6. illustrious
7. gifted
8. achievements
9. coaxed
10. coveted
Down
2. aspire
3. acclaimed
5. consistency

Test day Tips Told
1. C
2. D
3. B
4. D
5. C
6. A
7. C
8. D
9. B
10. C
11. A
12. A

Deep Freeze Down Under
pages 78-82

What's Your Opinion?
F, O, F, O

No Sweat with the Alphabet!
definition / pizza
degrees
glaciers
place / school
plains
recorded
research
schwa / television
scientists
shelters
surface
tell / trouble
temperature
tropical

Words and Meanings Together Again
1. f
2. h
3. d
4. g
5. a
6. b
7. i
8. j
9. e
10. c

Lost Words Return to Sentences
1. surface
2. shelters
3. recorded
4. degrees
5. tropical
6. temperature
7. research
8. glaciers
9. scientists
10. plains

Confusion Taken Out of Multiple Meanings
1. b
2. a
3. a
4. b
5. b
6. a
7. a
8. b

Solve This Scrambled Word Puzzle
1. surface
2. shelters
3. scientists
4. tropical
5. temperature
6. degrees
7. glaciers
8. plains
9. recorded
10. research

Improve Your Score
1. C
2. D
3. A
4. D
5. B
6. A
7. C
8. B
9. D
10. B
11. C
12. B

Hang in at Zero G!
pages 83-87

What's Your Conclusion?
a training wall that gives visitors the feeling of weightlessness

Alphabet Puts Words in Order
academic / church
astronauts
campers
catapults
churn / heavy
circular
course
gaseous
gravity
mental / still
simulator
wallet / zinc
weightless
zero

Meanings Found After Long Search
1.	e	6.	a
2.	j	7.	f
3.	g	8.	d
4.	c	9.	h
5.	i	10.	b

Investigate the Holes in These Stories
1.	circular	6.	simulator
2.	astronauts	7.	gravity
3.	campers	8.	weightless
4.	gaseous	9.	catapults
5.	zero	10.	course

New Endings . . .
1. backward
2. southward
3. eastward
4. seaward
5. northward
6. westward

Analogies Have Meaningful Relationships
1. catapults
2. backward
3. astronauts
4. snarl
5. nest
6. oven
7. include
8. curved
9. length
10. eyes

Secrets to Success on Tests
1.	D	7.	A
2.	B	8.	C
3.	A	9.	B
4.	D	10.	D
5.	B	11.	B
6.	D	12.	A

Kwanzaa—Candles, Culture, and Creativity
pages 93-97

Draw Your Own Conclusion
obtaining goods

Alphabet Orders Words
allow / cure
ancestors
celebration
culture
heart / pursue
heritage
principles
purpose
record / upward
represent
symbols
traditional
unity

Lost Meanings Found
1.	d	6.	g
2.	i	7.	e
3.	j	8.	a
4.	f	9.	h
5.	c	10.	b

Words Complete Sentences
1.	ancestors	6.	heritage
2.	purpose	7.	culture
3.	celebration	8.	represent
4.	traditional	9.	principles
5.	symbols	10.	unity

Pieces and Parts—Put Them Together
1. independent not dependent
2. insincere   not sincere
3. incomplete   not complete
4. invisible   not visible
5. indirect   not direct
6. inaccurate   not accurate
7. insecure   not secure
8. inexpensive not expensive
9. inconsiderate not considerate
10. indivisible   not divisible

Between One Thing and Another—Analogies
1. seek
2. unity
3. base
4. major
5. faded
6. independence
7. fingers
8. ancestors
9. wool
10. bracelet

Test-taking Secrets Revealed
1.	B	7.	C
2.	A	8.	D
3.	D	9.	B
4.	B	10.	B
5.	C	11.	C
6.	A	12.	B

Lucky Duck Takes Off
pages 88-92

Conclusions Found
to do the kind of TV she wanted to do

The Amazing Alphabet
accept / guilt
award
considers
discuss
episode
guise / react
invites
producer
programs
read / tail
reporters
success
take / voyage
viewers

Words and Meanings—A Perfect Match
1.	b	6.	g
2.	d	7.	e
3.	f	8.	c
4.	h	9.	j
5.	i	10.	a

112

New Words Complete Sentences
1.	success	6.	producer
2.	award	7.	episode
3.	programs	8.	viewers
4.	invites	9.	reporters
5.	discuss	10.	considers

Get to the Root of It
1.	cover	13.	approve
2.	read	14.	child
3.	child	15.	free
4.	comic	16.	doubt
5.	order	17.	discuss
6.	success	18.	time
7.	order	19.	cheer
8.	summer	20.	pay
9.	finish	21.	port
10.	state	22.	hope
11.	affect	23.	sincere
12.	wood	24.	limp

Close Study Reveals Hidden Words
```
S U C C E S S R S A C C S
M U D E C L I R M P G O M
E P I S O D E A I T A N A
R A G C I W I L E N T S R
G E U C E S N I I E R I G
D O I O E V V A W A R D O
T C O N V I E V E P E R
X R E P O R T E R S I R P
P R O D U C E R I T A S T
D I S C U S S R I O U S E
```

Test Your Best
1.	D	5.	C	9.	C
2.	B	6.	D	10.	D
3.	A	7.	B	11.	A
4.	D	8.	B	12.	B

Body Sends Mixed-up Messages
pages 98-102

Conclusions Flow from Story
to teach you something

Guide Words Relieve Stress
braid / eject
brain
certainly
elate / net
elbow
flowing
nerve
new / time
poisonous
pressure
tinfoil / worst
tingles
wastes
worry

Match Words and Meanings
1.	f	6.	a
2.	c	7.	e
3.	d	8.	g
4.	h	9.	i
5.	b	10.	j

Incomplete Sentences
1. elbow
2. pressure
3. wastes
4. worry
5. poisonous
6. flowing
7. certainly
8. tingles
9. nerve
10. brain

Homonym Confusion
1.	waste-waist	a.	waist
2.	prey-pray	b.	hear
3.	flour-flower	c.	blew
4.	blew-blue	d.	right
5.	cent-sent	e.	flour
6.	steal-steel		
7.	hear-here		
8.	right-write		
9.	tail-tale		
10.	threw-through		

Categories Help Words
1. arms, legs, body
2. trash can, disposal, sewer
3. skin, muscle, bone
4. water, blood, gasoline
5. insect sprays, cleaning liquids, house plants
6. nervous, headache, upset stomach
7. sight, smell, speech

Score Higher on Tests
1.	B	7.	C
2.	A	8.	B
3.	D	9.	D
4.	C	10.	A
5.	A	11.	B
6.	A	12.	A